# THE Art OF Balancing Soil Nutrients

## A Practical Guide to Interpreting Soil Tests

William "Crop Doc" McKibben

# The Art of Balancing Soil Nutrients
## A Practical Guide to Interpreting Soil Tests

The information in this book is true and complete to the best of our knowledge. All recommendations are made without guarantee on the part of the author and Acres U.S.A. The author and publisher disclaim any liability in connection with the use or misuse of this information.

Acres U.S.A.
P.O. Box 91299
Austin, Texas 78709 U.S.A.
(512) 892-4400 • fax (512) 892-4448
info@acresusa.com • www.acresusa.com

*Printed in the United States of America*

Publisher's Cataloging-in-Publication

McKibben, William L., 1952–
The art of balancing soil nutrients: a practical guide to
    interpreting soil tests / William L. McKibben—1st ed.,
    Austin, TX, Acres U.S.A., 2012
        vii, 240 pp., 26 cm
    Includes Index
    ISBN 978-1-60173-032-9 (trade)

1. Soils — analysis. 2. Soil testing. 3. Crops — soil fertility.
4. Agriculture — crops & soils. 5. Plant — nutrition.
I. McKibben, William L., 1952–   II. Title.
    S593.M35 2012        631.4

# Dedication

There are many people that I would like to thank with this dedication. First, I would like to thank those in the Brookside Laboratories organization, especially Bob Boehle, Jim Peck and Dick Psolla, who helped me when I first started consulting on soils.

Also, I would like to thank Susan Shaner and her staff at Logan Labs for their help in developing criteria for the paste analysis. In particular, Michelle Mahoney and Teresa Bambauer were extremely helpful in setting up the data analysis pages found throughout this book. I would also like to thank Susan Shaner for allowing me to work with her lab and give my assistance and recommendations to hundreds of people who had soils analyzed in her lab. It was the result of talking to a variety of clients of Logan Labs that I saw a real need to write this book in order to help people interpret their soil analysis reports.

I would also like to thank my good friend and mentor, Mike Hunter, for passing along his passionate quest for finding answers to many perplexing questions.

Lastly, but not in any way the least, I would like to thank my wife, Paula, for her encouragement over many years to write this book.

# Preface

This book is by no means the final chapter on interpreting soil analyses. The ideas on these pages are from my field observations, private studies and research done during the last 33 years of soil consulting. I view the information contained in this book to be a starting point for those who are taking soil samples and those wanting to have the best interpretations of the results possible. I realize that soils all over the world are highly variable depending upon their environmental conditions; however, chemical reactions are consistent around the world and vary mainly by their rate of reaction and degree of completion.

It is my hope that after reading this book you will be able to look at the data from your soils and then be able to make a rational interpretation of it.

I seriously doubt if there will ever be an *absolute* soil data recommendation due to the complexity and vast number of variables in the soil. Besides soil chemistry, soil physics and soil biology have an impact on root development, nutrient availability and nutrient intake. The goal whenever I give soil test results recommendations has always been to grow the biggest and highest quality crops, but not at the expense of depleting soil health. By striving to grow the biggest yields, you will in turn return the highest amount of organic residue back to the soil and maintain the most critical portion of the soil, organic matter or humus.

This book covers the interpretation of standard soil reports as well as those using paste analysis. With this information I believe you can apply the principles of soil balance to all your crops and soils. I believe that soils must be balanced by using both the basic cation saturation ratio (BCSR) and strategic level of available nutrient (SLAN) principles. There is much controversy among agronomists and soil consultants as to which method should be used for soil recommendations. Using the standard soil tests (Mehlich or ammonium acetate extractions), balance can be achieved nicely by using BCSR on soils with total exchange capacities (TEC) greater than 10. However, on soils with a TEC less than 5 the SLAN approach should be the main method. For soils with TEC between 5 and 10, a combination of BCSR and SLAN seems to work the best.

Paste analysis is extremely valuable for soils with lighter soil exchange capacities, however I find value with using them on the heavier soils as well. Paste analysis need not be used exclusively on soils primarily made up of calcareous sands or soilless media.

This approach to balancing soils using the various tests and methods available will be thoroughly covered in this book and illustrated with actual soil analysis examples. After reading this book you will know what I know; and then I ask you to build upon this and pass the information along about interpreting soil test results to others.

# Contents

# Figures

*Chapter 1*

# Soil Nutrient Preview

As an introduction, this chapter is designed to help the soil novice better understand the nutrients and their relationship within the soil. It is these nutrients that are important for plant growth and which will be discussed in detail in the later chapters about how they can be manipulated to improve plant growth.

In order to keep things in perspective and so that we do not get delusions of grandeur concerning our ability to affect plant growth, if you get a chance to look at the *Feeds and Nutrition* book written by M.E. Ensminger, J.E. Oldfield and W.W. Heinemann and turn to the analysis section on various feeds, you will find a very complete analysis of nearly all feedstuffs fed to livestock.

These feedstuffs all have a value listed for the ash content. This is the percentage of ash leftover after the carbon, hydrogen and oxygen have been burned off as carbon dioxide and water. Most of the "whole plant" feedstuffs listed, such as corn silage and grass silage, have ash values between 5-10%. The ash value represents virtually all the minerals found in the original plants. This information is significant and tells us that no matter how many nutrients we add to the soil, we cannot impact more than 10% of the total weight of the plant.

Therefore let us not forget that the nutrient balance is the key—not maximizing nutrient quantity. It is the things that have an impact on the water, soil oxygen content, and $CO_2$ exchange that are the factors that will affect 90% of what we want to grow, regardless of whether it is turfgrass, soybeans or corn.

With the importance of the nutrient balance in mind, let's look at the various nutrients and some of the relationships that exist between them.

I will start with the big three macronutrients, nitrogen, phosphorus and potassium. These are the primary nutrients listed when you buy a bag of fertilizer. For example, if you purchase a bag of 9-23-30 fertilizer at the store, the ratio on your bag is listed as NPK and will contain 9% nitrogen, 23% phosphorus (as $P_2O_5$) and 30% potassium (as $K_2O$). The phosphorus and potassium are listed as "oxides" since they don't typically exist in nature as pure elements. This does not mean that the elements that you are buying are in the oxide form, though. More than likely the phosphorus and nitrogen will exist as ammonium phosphate and the potassium will be a salt of either potassium chloride or potassium sulfate.

Most high concentration fertilizers are sold as a salt form. This is not necessarily a bad thing. A salt is nothing more than the combination of a strong base and a strong acid. For example, potassium sulfate when broken apart is a strong base of potassium hydroxide and a strong acid known as sulfuric acid. Epsom salts or magnesium sulfate ($MgSO_4$) is the combination of sulfuric acid and magnesium hydroxide.

Salts that are made up of strong acids and strong bases are electrically neutral in their charge and will not raise the pH (level of acidity or alkalinity) of the soil. Therefore gypsum, which is calcium sulfate ($CaSO_4$) and is made up of a strong base of calcium hydroxide and a strong acid of sulfuric acid, when added to the soil does not change the soil pH. On the other hand, a salt of calcium carbonate (lime) will move the soil pH upward (more alkaline) because it is made up of the combination of a strong base, calcium hydroxide and a weak acid known as carbonic acid.

----

## Nitrogen

Nitrogen is a major contributing nutrient responsible for plant growth. Plants deficient in nitrogen will be yellow, spindly and shorter than normal. Although all the plant nutrients are critical, none seem to produce such a quick and dramatic effect on plant growth as nitrogen does. It is because of this reason that nitrogen has been over-used and abused.

Excess use of chemical nitrogen in forms such as urea, ammonium sulfate, ammonium nitrate, calcium nitrate, and anhydrous ammonia, just to name a few, will lower soil organic matter levels when they are applied. Microbes break down nitrogen sources in order to maintain an approximate 20:1 ratio of carbon to nitrogen in the soil. This source of carbon could come from plant residues or soil organic matter. Manures generally provide a source of carbon from the original livestock bedding. The overuse of manures, though, can cause nitrogen (and phosphorus) contamination of our water resources.

## Phosphorus

Phosphorus supplies the energy for the plant. This nutrient is critical in the photosynthesis process whereby light energy is converted to chemical energy within the plant. Plants that are deficient of phosphorus will tend to be lighter in color, short and many times will display a reddish coloration from the accumulation of sugars in the plant. Phosphorus may be deficient in the plant despite having adequate soil levels available—if nitrogen, magnesium or zinc is also deficient.

Any nutrient that affects root growth, such as calcium or boron, may impact phosphorus levels in the plant too since phosphorus is very immobile in the soil. Phosphorus will also form layers and stratify very easily on the soil surface (even in sandy soils) if some sort of incorporation isn't done.

## Potassium

Potassium is a real workhorse nutrient that affects disease resistance, grain or fruit quality, water efficiency, and carbohydrate movement in the plant. Potassium is like the radiator fluid in your car, acting as an antifreeze during frosty conditions and a summer coolant in high heat weather. Plants deficient in potassium require more water, have lower carbohydrate contents, and are more attractive to insect pests.

Potassium deficiency is generally exhibited on the lower leaves since potassium is highly mobile in the plant and easily transported to the new growth. The older leaves will exhibit yellowing on the leaf margin or on the outside edge of the leaf—eventually dying and dropping off. It is for this reason that forages will tend to be more fibrous in a feed analysis when they are growing on a potassium-deficient soil.

Plants containing high levels of protein or carbohydrates generally also have a high demand for potassium. The removal of potassium by a crop is often 4-5 times less than what the plants need to uptake in order to produce a top yield. For example, a corn crop of 180 bushels per acre will remove approximately 30-35 lbs. of potassium (or 36-42 lbs. of $K_2O$). However, the plants must be able to uptake nearly 210 lbs. of potassium (or 250 lbs. of $K_2O$) to get this amount. When building potassium levels in the soil remember potassium will compete with magnesium uptake.

## Sulfur

Sulfur is an element that growers may see as deficient in upcoming years as the atmosphere is now containing less and less sulfur dioxide as a result of mandated emission controls. Much of the sulfur in the soil is taken up into plants as an anion (an ion with a negative charge because it contains more electrons than protons). The sulfur is converted into amino acids or enzymes with the primary function being to aid in the reduction conversion of nitrates into proteins and amino acids. Consequently, sulfur deficiencies look a lot like nitrogen deficiencies but are not as dramatic as a nitrogen deficency. Plants are generally smaller and lighter in color.

In tissue analysis, nitrogen deficiencies also tend to show a higher level of sulfur deficiencies. There is a strong correlation between nitrogen and sulfur, consequently, as nitrogen application rates are increased so must the sulfur levels increase.

## Calcium

Calcium is the facilitator for all nutrients going into and out of the plant because of the impact of this element on cellular integrity and root development. Calcium is critical to plants for soil pH control, as it influences nutrient solubility and ultimately the control of nutrient uptake in the plant. Calcium can impact soil structure by flocculating clays (breaking them up into flakes) therefore improving water movement and aeration in the soil.

No other nutrient crosses over between soil chemistry and soil physics like calcium. Calcium deficiencies show up first in the new growth and the ability of the plants to stand upright. Root mass will also be restricted if this nutrient is deficient. A classic calcium deficiency in tomatoes, for example, will show up as blossom end rot in the fruiting tissue. A calcium deficiency in soils might also result in manganese toxicity due to a low soil pH when the lack of calcium causes a sharp increase in manganese solubility.

## Magnesium

Magnesium is most often associated with chlorophyll formation in plants. Without magnesium there would be no chlorophyll or green plants—the basis of life on earth. Based on this aspect alone, magnesium is a powerful nutrient, but it is also very important for phosphorus uptake in the plant. Magnesium deficiency looks a lot like manganese deficiency with its interveinal chlorosis (dark green veins and light green between veins). Since magnesium is also involved in phosphorus uptake, some plants may take on a reddish color like that shown by phosphorus deficiency. Magnesium deficiencies are more prevalent in sandy soils but can be induced in heavier soils due to high potassium, ammonium or calcium applications.

## Trace Elements

Boron, iron, manganese, copper, zinc and molybdenum are considered trace elements due to the small amount of the nutrient needed for plant growth. These nutrients are primarily involved in highly complex enzymatic systems within the plant. They all enhance plant chemical reactions without necessarily becoming part of the reaction. Therefore they can be recycled in the plant and require very small quantities of each element, hence the term trace elements. These reactions stimulated by trace elements are at the cellular or intracellular level and even today are not fully understood by soil and plant scientists.

The degree of trace element availability in plants is certainly driven by the overall quantities of the nutrients in the soil but even more so, their availability is driven by soil pH and microbial activity. The solubility of the trace elements is significantly reduced as soil pH approaches 7 and goes higher. Conversely, the solubility significantly increases at lower pH levels to the point that trace elements can become toxic at pH levels of 5 and below.

The trace elements also all have a pH range in which they are deficient but do not show visual symptoms. Tissue sampling at various times during the growing season is the only way to head off these problems. Once the visual symptoms show up, the plants are in severe trouble dramatically reducing yield and quality.

## How Should I Apply Trace Elements?

In setting up many soil recommendations, I find myself recommending a trace element ranging from 0.25 lbs./1,000 sq. ft. up to 1.0 lbs./1,000 sq. ft. I often wonder just how well these trace elements are being applied. Blending traces with other dry fertilizers is currently the method of choice, but is it really the best? Dry fertilizers can range in weight from 30 to 60 lbs. per cubic foot. Trace elements tend to weigh in at the upper range. Then there is particle size, which can range from dust to large granules. After blending, separation during transport to the site and during application is a concern.

Foliar feeding is by far the best and most effective way to apply traces in the agricultural sector but for turf, this is not very practical when you're cutting grass every day.

Impregnating highly concentrated liquid traces onto the dry bulk fertilizer is a very effective and efficient way to apply your trace elements. There are flowable trace elements on the market which weigh 15 lbs. per gallon and have 0.5 lbs. of metal ions per pint. These will cost more than the dry, but are still cheaper than the chelates. When impregnating trace elements, it is important to choose the right fertilizer. Avoid putting the traces on your phosphate sources of fertilizer. Phosphates can tie up readily with zinc and manganese. It is better to use dry potassium and nitrogen fertilizers as your carriers. The amount of traces elements will depend on your removal rate and starting levels currently in your soil.

*The Soil Probe Newsletter, Logan Labs*

## Boron

Boron is an anion, which is involved in many essential processes within the plant. This element is associated with energy transformation reactions, carbohydrate transport, blossom retention, reduction in seed blanks, and is critical for root elongation. Boron is highly influenced by cations—especially calcium. High levels of calcium in the soil will reduce boron solubility and availability. On the flip side, tissues with low boron levels tend to show more calcium deficncies. Potassium uptake is improved with good boron levels in the plants. Boron is moved primarily in the water transport system (xylem), therefore foliar feeding with boron will do little to impact roots. As a result of having to make this movement through the xylem, foliar tissue tests seem to come up with more boron deficiencies during cold, wet conditions with symptoms visually showing up primarily at the growing points.

## Iron

Iron is a nutrient which is highly involved in the chlorophyll reaction helping to contribute to the green coloration of plants. It is this nutrient that is found in high concentrations in soils and makes up part of the clay structure. Iron like manganese is more available to plants in the reduced form, consequently the better the aeration in the soil the less available both iron and manganese become.

Iron deficiencies seem to be the result more from an interference issue from other ions rather than from low levels in the soil. This is not the case for organic soils, which are inherently low in iron and manganese.

Iron is not easily translocated within the plant and must be available in a continual supply during the growing season. It is for this reason that iron deficiencies tend to show up first on the new growth. Oftentimes tissue analysis will show very high levels of aluminum and iron. This is especially true of samples collected early in the growing season and cut close to the ground. These high levels are generally the result of soil  contamination of the tissue sample. High levels of bicarbonate in the irrigation water also will reduce iron availability.

---

## Manganese

Manganese, like so many of the other trace elements, is involved in a multitude of reactions within the plant. Manganese levels will impact disease resistance, nitrogen utilization, photosynthesis, water utilization, and cold tolerance (just to name a few). This nutrient is highly reactive to its environmental conditions. Loose, well-aerated, and high pH soils substantially reduce the availability of manganese.

According to Dr. Don Huber from Purdue University the application of glyphosate/Roundup will tie up manganese within the plant as well as alter the microbial populations in the rhizosphere from reduction to oxidation, which lowers the availability of manganese. Other trace elements such as copper, iron and zinc have been implicated in this phenomenon. I have seen manganese levels in glyphosate-resistant plants be reduced by 50% following an herbicide application.

## Copper

Copper plays many roles in plants but the two most prevalent areas are involved with nitrogen utilization and lignum formation. Copper will improve nitrogen utilization and the formation of proteins. As nitrogen is increased in the crop fertility program so must the level of copper in the plant be increased. The ability of grasses to stand upright will significantly improve with adequate copper levels in the plant. Plants short of copper oftentimes have below average root mass due to nutrient limitations, compaction, saturated conditions or root pruning.

High levels of phosphorus and potassium can have a detrimental reaction of inducing deficiencies of copper as well as iron. Copper has been shown to reduce head blights in wheat. A good indication that wheat is deficient in copper is when you see that the heads do not come out of the whorl properly and get pinched on the tip and bow.

## Zinc

Zinc is highly involved in the reproductive side of plant chemistry. Corn, soybeans and fruit trees are especially sensitive to zinc deficiencies. This nutrient is not very mobile in plants and generally deficiencies show up early in the growing season. Plants will tend to be smaller and lighter in color if zinc is lacking. Corn will demonstrate a light striping in the leaves, and dicot plants will exhibit smaller leaves near the growing point as an indication of zinc deficiency. The numbers of rows around an ear of corn can also be greatly influenced by the level of zinc and phosphorus in the plant—especially at the V5-V6 stage or when the corn plant is about 10-12 inches tall.

Plants do a better job of phosphorus uptake when the zinc levels are adequate. High soil pH levels and heavy phosphorus applications will reduce zinc availability substantially. Those applying manure seem to have better availability of zinc as shown in the tissue data. The demand for zinc in plants is high early in the growing season. Seed treatment using zinc is very helpful, but will last only 30-35 days before foliar treatments will be necessary as the plant grows.

## Molybdenum

Molybdenum like boron is taken up as an anion. When looking at the availability of trace elements based on pH, molybdenum is opposite of the other traces and has the effect of increasing in availability as the pH increases. Keeping the pH between 6.2 and 6.5 is best for all the trace elements except molybdenum. Molybdenum is highly involved in nitrogen assimilation in the plant, therefore molybdenum deficiencies tend to look like nitrogen deficiencies. High levels of phosphorus in the soil will reduce molybdenum uptake.

Yellowing along the leaf margins as well as a tendency for the leaf to cup upward may be an indication of molybdenum deficiency. Molybdenum is not extremely mobile in the plant and that is why the deficiency will almost always be seen on the new growth.

Legumes demonstrate a high accumulation of molybdenum in the nitrogen-forming nodules. Maintaining an adequate soil pH is the best way to supply molybdenum.

---

## Fixing the Problem

I receive many soil reports with a request for help from a variety of individuals who want me to help them fix their soil. I thoroughly enjoy the challenge, but oftentimes wonder just how well I accomplish the goal. Whether you try to fix the soil or to balance the soil, it is never a short-term job. It is a continual and long-term endeavor. The problem when working with soils, and I truly mean "with soils," is when it comes to soil fertility one plus one rarely if ever equals two. Can we ever achieve the perfect balance? I don't think so. All we can be certain of is Nature, itself, is always in a state of flux and change. When left alone, nature seems to minimize the degree of flux and the speed at which it occurs. It would be like looking at an oscilloscope and seeing a gentle wave going across the screen representing the way in nature. But nature does not have to worry about time or productivity; therefore, when humans enter the picture trying to maximize production through monocultures, the wave on the oscilloscope becomes higher and more rapid. The trick is to keep it from going out of control and leaving the screen black or the soils dead. Prof. Albrecht has given us some great guidelines in which to start our soil balance practices. These are by no means the end-all in balancing soils. Solubility testing along with tissue sampling is needed to move to the next level.

The individuals who say that they can fix all your soil problems by adding this product or that product suffer from a complete lack of soils knowledge or delusions of grandeur. Soils are very dynamic and any fertilizer additions will cause the wave on the oscilloscope to vacillate wildly. This doesn't mean we need to throw up our hands in desperation. It just means every action has a reaction and we must be very patient when attempting to manipulate soil fertility. Testing and retesting the soils is important, along with asking the plants  by means of tissue sampling what they think of the changes we have made.

There are a couple of things that one must consider when reading a soil report to make recommendations for change. First, the soil collected for the test should be a representative sample of the entire area. It will represent both the high and low fertility areas, now combined into a good average. Secondly, depth of the soil sample will affect the outcome of the test and tells you nothing of the nutritional levels at the various depths of the sample. Many assume that once the report comes back that the level of nutrition reported by the lab is constant through the sampling profile. Nothing could be further from the truth,  especially samples in minimum or no tillage areas. Without thorough mixing, nutrients applied to the surface of the soil will move at different rates and depths depending on the solubility and chemical interactions. Phosphorus,  for example will move normally less than a half an inch in the soil because of its highly reactive nature. Nutrient stratification will not be a problem for plant growth, providing root activity is maintained in that area and the nutrients are mobile in the phloem of the plants. In the phloem of the plant, nutrients can move up or down depending on the need. If the soils go dry in these high fertility zones and root activity ceases, deficiencies will likely occur. There is one nutrient that soil stratification is a real problem, and that is calcium.

Calcium is primarily xylem mobile. This means it travels through the plant in the water transport system and moves upward almost exclusively. Calcium, which is needed for cell wall development, cannot be translocated from roots higher in the soil profile where calcium is in excess to roots lower in the soil profile needing calcium. Most lime samples that we have analyzed are only 5% soluble at a pH of 7.0. Liming soils with a relatively low pH will increase the solubility of the lime only if the lime is adequately incorporated. Lime left on the surface will rapidly increase the pH at the surface and lower the solubility of the lime to approximately 5%. Because lime applications are made in large quantities, the phosphorus in the limed zones can precipitate out, reducing the availability.

With these facts in mind, let's look at sample that came across my desk early in September. The area in question was planted to a groundcover in July which by September was still not growing. There was concern whether the planting would make it through the winter. The soil sample showed very low phosphorus and low potassium. Phosphorus is critical for maintaining energy in the plant. Plants deficient in phosphorus are often short and exhibit a red to purple color on the leaves or stems. Potassium helps in disease resistance and moisture utilization. Potassium can aid plants during the summer in water movement for cooling and act as an antifreeze during the winter. The pH of the soil was at 7.5 which makes phosphorus deficiencies twice as bad. My suggestion was to remove the ground cover and apply a very heavy application of phosphorus and potassium and incorporate to 6-7 inches, then replant the ground cover. The soil exchange capacity was very low making it extremely difficult to get effective use out of a top dress application of fertilizer, since the soils could not be kept moist enough at the surface to maintain root activity. This was a lot of work for the individual, however, in the long run it will prove to be the most successful. Although no solubility test was run on this sample, I suspect that low soluble calcium and magnesium levels may exist, even though the pH was 7.5. When exchange capacities drop below 10, the soils are usually very sandy making it hard to hold any nutrients. I would encourage individuals with low exchange capacity soils to run both the standard soil test as well as a solubility analysis. For soils with exchange capacities above 10, run the standard test and see if the soil level of the nutrients are adequate. If so, call the lab and ask for a solubility test to make sure the nutrients are available in solution.

*The Soil Probe Newsletter, Logan Labs*

*Chapter 2*

# Taking a Soil Sample

---

IT IS IMPORTANT TO UNDERSTAND HOW SAMPLING CAN AFFECT THE quality of result data before we even start our discussion on balancing soils, desired nutrient levels, or threshold levels. Knowing the history of what you are sampling may dramatically affect what and how you collect for your testing samples.

Some questions to ask before sampling:

1. When was the last fertilizer application?
2. What kind of tillage, if any, has there been over the last 10 years?
3. What depth are we concerned with? Which crop is being grown?
4. How has the fertilizer been applied (banded, broadcast, deep placement, etc.)?
5. What kind of fertilizer was applied?

Ideally it would be best to collect soil samples that are located the farthest from any type of fertilizer application. This may not be possible and as long as one realizes that the results may be affected adjustments can be made. Adjusting soil fertility is in no way a short, quick and easy trip, but rather a continual journey. It is much the same as a pilot who sets out to fly across the country to a certain destination far away. The pilot must continually adjust the direction of the plane to compensate for wind and storms along the way.

Most fertilizers that are applied these days are quite soluble and when there has been a couple of inches of rain or irrigation, the fertilizer will dissolve. Until an equilibrium of nutrients is reached in the soil, the test data can be affected. Even though the application may only be one nutrient—for example, potash, it can increase the level of other nutrients in the soil test. The dissolved potassium may act as an extractant and displace cations such as calcium and magnesium off the soil colloids.

The depths of soil sampling can also vary depending on the crop being grown. My rule of thumb is sample to the depth of the main root mass. If the root mass is shallower than it should be, two samples may be the best option. The first sample depth should go to the existing level of the root mass and the second sample would continue to the desired root growth depth. This would allow you to determine if the lower depth has some deficiency or toxicity present which is restricting root development.

> The dry weight of soil (sandy loam) in 1 inch = 330,000 lbs. per acre.

One of most important sampling techniques is controlling the sample depth. Many times I get asked a question about interpreting soil sample results such as, "What might have caused the soil values to have such a significant drop or increase from the previous sample?" My first thought when asked this is about sample depth.

Research has found that there is a 17% variable when your sampling depth varies by only an inch from the previous sampling depth (when done at a 6 inch depth). This is why I developed a soil probe with a foot peg on the body of it to control the sampling depth. The sample depth is determined by sliding the probe in or out to the desired depth, inserting the pin and pressing down (Figure 1). It is impossible to plot the nutritional direction of a field, golf green or fairway if the depth is not controlled. Samples tend to show a significant drop in their nutrient levels from one year to another, in spite of fertilizer maintenance programs. This is generally due to a lack of consistency in sampling depth.

This raises a concern I have noticed that has been rapidly increasing as agriculture moves to more and more conservation tillage and no-till. This concern is already quite obvious in many turfgrass samples that I have observed. This problem occurs as a result of the stratification (or layering) of nutrients.

# Soil Testing Probe with Depth Control Feature

**Fig. 1** *Here is a soil testing probe with a depth control foot peg and an adjustable sampling tube. Adjust the depth by removing the pin and sliding the tube to the desired depth. Here sampling depth is set at 6 inches.*

It is extremely important to realize that data collected from the core soil samples reflects an average of all the layers within that profile area. The data should not be construed as being all the same for the total depth unless some aggressive tillage such as moldboard plowing is being done.

The stratification or layering of nutrients may be very high at the surface, but often will get progressively worse with more depth. As soils dry out and root activity is lost at the surface, plants may now be seeking nutrition deeper in the soil where the nutrients may be deficient. This may be one reason why soil tests, which look similar on paper, may look dramatically different for the crops in the field. A soil with nutrients evenly distributed throughout the profile should be expected to perform better during dry conditions. Conversely, a soil with stratified phosphorus in the surface region may do better during cool, spring weather when microbial activity is reduced, but activity may slow down or even stall as the soils dry out and root activity declines in the surface region.

Notice the soil test in Figure 3 which compares the soil results from the same greens sampled at two and six inches in depth. These are U.S. Golf Association (USGA) golf greens, which are primarily made up of sand. Notice the level of nutrients that are in the top two inches in comparison to the results for the 6 inch depth. Calculation based on the results indicate that 69% of the phosphorus, 62% of the calcium, 53% of the magnesium and 60% of the potassium are all in the top two inches of the profile.

Now consider the nutrient stratification effect of a soil that has some clay and higher organic levels. Here the movement of nutrients will be even shallower because of the many more exchange sites that clay contains. The ramifications of this stratification situation will be discussed later. The fact of the matter is that losing any part of the surface while sampling or exceeding the optimum depth will have dramatic results on the data.

These sampling errors make it almost impossible to compare historical data. Be careful not to lose any of the topsoil layers when conditions are dry and be aware of the importance of soil sampling depth during moist conditions.

Turf managers often ask if they should take off the sod portion of a core sample before putting it into the sample bag. Put everything in the sample bag and let the lab screen off the organic residue from the top. Notice the difference in the following soil samples (Figure 2) that were taken side by side with the only difference being that the sod was pinched off by the golf superintendent. The samples are fairly close for most nutrients with the exception of phosphorus and zinc, which stratify very easily.

# Soil Sampling Tools

Bill McKibben has developed a sampling probe which has an adjustable sampling depth and is completely stainless steel. This will be the last soil probe you will ever buy. Here are some questions regarding the soil probe and the cost.

**Q: Why develop a new probe when there are already many on the market?**

A: The main reason for developing this probe was to improve the accuracy of sampling by controlling the sampling depth.

**Q: What's the big deal about controlling the depth?**

A: There are two reasons for controlling the sampling depth. First, the amount of additives used will depend on the amount of soil that we are trying to adjust. Typically a 6" sample represents 2,000,000 pounds on a one-acre area. Varying the soil sample depth by one inch, results in the amount of soil represented being different by 330,000 pounds. Understanding the soil volume is no different than knowing a volume of water in which a fertilizer will be added for a foliar application. This becomes very critical for lighter soils with a low TEC. Secondly, year to year comparisons of soil tests don't mean much if the depth is not controlled.

**Q: Where might depth control of the soil samples be less important?**

A: Depth control is always best. However, in situations where the soils are being plowed on a yearly basis, we can assume a more homogeneous mixing of the soil resulting in the depth control not be as consequential. This is certainly not the case for most soils at the present time and definitely not the case on a golf course.

**Q: What is the core sample size?**

A: The core size is 1/2 inch. I like this size because I can take more probes per composite sample, which helps to increase accuracy. This may mean a little more work, but it's well worth it for the increased accuracy in the recommendations. With fertilizers well over $600 per ton, accuracy is even more critical.

**Q: What is the cost for the probe and why?**

A: The cost for the probe is currently just under $300. The cost seems like a lot, but this will be the last probe you ever buy. The probe is made completely of stainless steel and meticulously manufactured in Ohio. If the soil tips wear out, a new tube can be inserted and you're back to basically a new probe. The tubes can be returned to the manufacturer and the tips replaced. There is over $100 in stainless in the probe without the manufacturing cost.

**Q: Do you see any other advantages to this probe?**

A: The major advantage to this probe is consistency of sampling depth, which is a huge factor especially when someone else is pulling samples. There are consultants who have three or four people sampling for them and having this probe would guarantee accuracy of sampling depth. Golf course superintendents whose job is on the line based on how the course looks and plays should insist on this type of probe whether they are doing their own recommendations or pulling samples for a consultant. Many of the samples I see coming across my desk are from a 3 or 4 inch depth. Moving as little as a half of an inch in sampling variability means 12-17% difference in your results.

**Q: What depth can this probe be adjusted to?**

A: This probe can be adjusted to 3, 4, 6, 8, 9 and 12 inches. Removing a pin and sliding the sampling tube up or down to the preferred depth can easily make these adjustments. The depth is controlled by the foot peg that helps tremendously in sampling dry or compacted soils.

*The Soil Probe Newsletter, Logan Labs*

# Country Club Turfgrass Comparison Soil Report

| Sample Location | | G18 | G18 |
|---|---|---|---|
| Sample ID | | w/ plug | w/o plug |
| Lab Number | | 1 | 2 |
| Sample Depth (inches) | | 6 | 6 |
| Total Exchange Capacity (m.e.) | | 10.42 | 11.91 |
| pH of Soil Sample | | 8.60 | 8.70 |
| Organic Matter (percent) | | 1.11 | 0.97 |
| **Anions** | SULFUR: p.p.m. | 18 | 14 |
| | Mehlich III Phosphorus: as ($P_2O_5$) lbs. / acre | 143 | 49 |
| **Exchangeable Cations** | CALCIUM: lbs. / acre Value Found | 3465 | 4098 |
| | MAGNESIUM: lbs. / acre Value Found | 252 | 238 |
| | POTASSIUM: lbs. / acre Value Found | 109 | 79 |
| | SODIUM: lbs. / acre | 126 | 116 |
| **Base Saturation %** | Calcium (60 to 70%) | 83.16 | 86.00 |
| | Magnesium (10 to 20%) | 10.08 | 8.32 |
| | Potassium (2 to 5%) | 1.34 | 0.85 |
| | Sodium (0.5 to 3%) | 2.63 | 2.12 |
| | Other Bases (Variable) | 2.80 | 2.70 |
| | Exchangeable Hydrogen (10 to 15%) | 0.00 | 0.00 |
| **Trace Elements** | Boron (ppm) | 0.26 | < 0.2 |
| | Iron (ppm) | 78 | 61 |
| | Manganese (ppm) | 44 | 33 |
| | Copper (ppm) | 1.37 | 1.02 |
| | Zinc (ppm) | 6.94 | 3.02 |
| | Aluminum (ppm) | 26 | 22 |

**Fig. 2** *Two side by side country club turfgrass soil samples taken at 6 inch depths with the only difference being that the sod was removed from the second sample (identified as w/o plug).*

Soil sampling after a tillage operation may have a profound effect on the results. For example, let us assume that our standard sampling depth is 7.5 inches and the field has been chisel plowed using 4 inch twisted shovels. Often these types of chisel plows appear to be going much deeper than they really are. If the plow is going five inches deep and the soil is rolled up the shank onto the undisturbed soil, the appearance is that the plow is really going deep—almost to 10 inches. The effect of the chisel plow on our sampling is the real question at hand. If our sampling depth is 7.5 inches you can see from the diagram on the next page that getting a true depth is virtually impossible when taking samples from worked soil. If we sampled from the top of the ridges, our core depth would have to be nearly 12.5 inches deep. With the top 5 inches removed we can get a sample that is somewhat representative of a field not tilled. Another factor in determining the correct soil sample depth is whether the tillage equipment was held at a constant depth.

# Tilled Soils Can Cause Sampling Problems

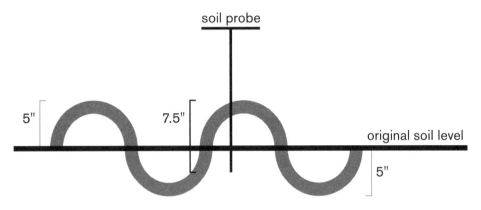

*Sampling becomes problematic when trying to get a uniform depth in plowed fields. To get a more accurate result, remove the ridge area down to the original soil level and then take a core to the desired depth.*

Soil testing depth is not an issue for fields that have been uniformly and consistently tilled with no soil ridges or valleys. Sampling a field that had been plowed following a long period of minimal tilling or no-tillage might result in some erratic results since the fertility is not uniformly mixed throughout the profile. The most consistent results will come from sampling fields prior to tillage operations.

# Country Club Turfgrass Comparison Soil Report

| Sample Location | | Green | Green | | Green | Green |
|---|---|---|---|---|---|---|
| Sample ID | | 6 | 6 | | 8 | 8 |
| Lab Number | | 5 | 2 | | 4 | 1 |
| Sample Depth (inches) | | 2 | 6 | | 2 | 6 |
| Total Exchange Capacity (m.e.) | | 9.77 | 5.58 | | 11.80 | 6.53 |
| pH of Soil Sample | | 7.00 | 6.80 | | 7.00 | 6.50 |
| Organic Matter (percent) | | 2.29 | 1.06 | | 2.40 | 1.06 |
| **Anions** | **SULFUR:** p.p.m. | 93 | 42 | | 105 | 53 |
| | **Mehlich III Phosphorus:** as ($P_2O_5$) lbs. / acre | 230 | 334 | | 278 | 392 |
| **Exchangeable Cations** | **CALCIUM:** lbs. / acre Value Found | 1071 | 1721 | | 1306 | 1929 |
| | **MAGNESIUM:** lbs. / acre Value Found | 74 | 140 | | 85 | 149 |
| | **POTASSIUM:** lbs. / acre Value Found | 73 | 122 | | 82 | 139 |
| | **SODIUM:** lbs. / acre | 16 | 53 | | 18 | 45 |
| **Base Saturation %** | Calcium (60 to 70%) | 82.21 | 77.07 | | 82.99 | 73.83 |
| | Magnesium (10 to 20%) | 9.47 | 10.45 | | 9.00 | 9.50 |
| | Potassium (2 to 5%) | 2.87 | 2.80 | | 2.67 | 2.73 |
| | Sodium (0.5 to 3%) | 1.06 | 2.04 | | 0.98 | 1.51 |
| | Other Bases (Variable) | 4.40 | 4.60 | | 4.40 | 4.90 |
| | Exchangeable Hydrogen (10 to 15%) | 0.00 | 3.00 | | 0.00 | 7.50 |
| **Trace Elements** | Boron (ppm) | 0.61 | 0.81 | | 0.66 | 0.72 |
| | Iron (ppm) | 265 | 222 | | 338 | 262 |
| | Manganese (ppm) | 280 | 196 | | 287 | 200 |
| | Copper (ppm) | 15.66 | 9.36 | | 17.47 | 10.6 |
| | Zinc (ppm) | 71.8 | 36.01 | | 88.75 | 41.48 |
| | Aluminum (ppm) | 113 | 92 | | 135 | 193 |
| **Other** | Bicarbonate | 88 | 73 | | 95 | 85 |
| | Silicon | | 13.2 | | | 17 |
| | | | | | | |
| | | | | | | |

**Fig. 3** *A soil report that compares two sites each sampled at 2 and 6 inch depths. Notice the high concentration of nutrients in the 0-2 inch depth sample.*

# Selecting a Soil Testing Laboratory

### WHEN IS THE BEST TIME TO DO A SOIL SAMPLE?

The best time to sample soil is *anytime* that is not directly affected by a nutrient application and at a time that is consistent from year to year. The weather will always be a factor, but it is important that we realize to a certain degree, that any soil sample collected is just a snapshot in time and its real value comes after the successive second and third samples are collected perhaps a year or two into the future. These follow up samples are important because they provide a trend line, and with this you will have a real direction and can make a plan for balancing the soils. That doesn't mean adjustments can't be made after the first sampling, but care should be taken so as to not overreact in making hasty nutrient corrections.

### WHERE SHOULD I COLLECT MY SAMPLES IN THE FIELD AND HOW MANY SAMPLES SHOULD I COLLECT?

It is always nice to have yield maps to help determine where sampling zones should be set up in a field, but this is not always possible. So, if no yield maps are available, start by sampling visible soil types. An even simpler strategy is to sample the high ground versus the low ground; this is at least a great place to start. Yields generally vary quite a lot from the low ground (black soils) to the light colored or high ground. Sampling these two types of areas generally will give you the broadest range of fertility issues possible.

The number of cores collected per composite sample will vary depending on the field size, but even in small fields, a minimum of 12-15 cores should provide an adequate amount of soil for the lab as well as make a good composite sample. Theoretically, there is one spot in the field that represents the composite, but since we don't know exactly where that spot is, a number of samples are necessary.

There is also no reason to sample areas in a field that will not get special treatment. For example, if you are sampling a 25-acre field with a 2-acre high spot in the back and you are not willing to treat that area,

*Sample high priority mgmt areas*

leave the high ground out of the composite and just sample the remaining 23 acres of low ground.

Sampling turfgrass is much easier since your areas are easily defined such as greens, tees, fairways, practice fields or game fields. Again, certainly problem areas within the larger sampling zone should be separated out.

### WHAT SHOULD I USE TO COLLECT THE SAMPLE?

The best way to prevent contamination of the sample is to collect a soil sample and place it directly into the bags provided by the laboratory. I prefer paper bags since the soil can air-dry on my shelves while waiting to go to the lab. Paper bags other than those provided by the lab may have glues that are water soluble—meaning the bags may fall apart—and the glues may also contain contaminates, both of which will affect the resulting soil data. Only once in my 32 years of consulting have I received bad bags from a lab. We had started noticing abnormally high boron levels in our samples. We notified the laboratory, which checked its equipment and found nothing amiss and then they looked at the bags only to find that the bag company had used the wrong glue. Over a half million bags were sent back. I like to use the labs' soil bags since the good labs will pretest their bags for potential contamination before they get into customers' hands.

### HOW DO I SELECT THE LABORATORY?

There are many good labs in the country. I have only used two in the past, Brookside Laboratories and now Logan Labs, both in Ohio. Good labs have a reasonable turnaround time and use up-to-date testing equipment such as inductively coupled plasma (ICP), nitrogen analyzers, auto-analyzers and auto-samplers, to name a few. Many also have computerized database systems that allow reports to be electronically transferred to further reduce turnaround time. Good labs will also participate in sample exchange programs to verify their results and have a quality control system in place at the laboratory.

The important point is to do your homework and find a good laboratory—then stick with them. Similar laboratories may run the same type of extraction method (such as Mehlich III or ammonium acetate), however, many other small details such as the ratio of extracting solution to soil, shaking time, shaking rate, or even the laboratory temperature may all have an effect on the accuracy of the results.

I can't stress enough, find a good lab that you like and stick with them. If you do have to change labs for any reason, spend a little extra money and run duplicate samples through both labs until you feel comfortable and understand any differences that may occur. There is no perfect soil test result number. By sending your duplicate samples to two different labs you are correlating each lab result with a predictable response in the field.

When I was with Brookside Laboratories the decision was made to switch from a hot water extraction for boron to a Mehlich extraction method. The Mehlich extraction yielded a number that was one tenth that of the result of the old hot water extraction method. So 1.0 ppm of boron from the Mehlich extraction was the same as 10.0 ppm from the old method. The last service that a good laboratory should offer is the ability to run a variety of tests such as the standard soil tests with trace nutrients, as well as paste, tissue and water analyses.

## Selecting a Soil Testing Laboratory

By Susan Shaner

How does anyone choose the right laboratory? Aren't they all the same? Should you send a sample to several different labs and average the results? How do you get the samples to a lab and what is the turnaround time?

Some homework needs to be done here.

These are all questions that I hear on almost a daily basis. All labs are not the same. This does not mean that one laboratory is better than another. They all provide a different "menu" of services. It is important to find a lab that provides all of the services that you require. Are you just looking for a soil analysis or do you also need an irrigation water test or tissue analysis?

Laboratories can also choose from a number of methods or recipes to obtain results. Which method would be best for your soil type or crop? Presentation of results can also vary greatly from one laboratory to another. It is important that you can read the report and make use of the information it provides. These are all questions that you should consider before choosing a laboratory.

**Menu of Services**

Packages with various soil parameters are usually available plus some a la carte choices. This will vary greatly from one laboratory to another. I think we all agree now that there is a lot more to soil than pH. Therefore, look at what is included in the soil package you are requesting. Important parameters include pH, organic matter, exchange capacity, and base saturation. Also important are the major elements calcium, magnesium, potassium, sodium and phosphorus. Important minor elements include sulfur, boron, iron, manganese, copper, zinc and aluminum. A complete soil analysis including all of these parameters may cost a little more. More information will provide better insight into your fertility situation. If you base your decision on cost alone, you will probably get what you pay for. An inexpensive analysis may only include pH, phosphorus and potassium.

**Methodology**

Methodology is the most confusing area when comparing laboratories. There are several different methods for almost every parameter on a soil analysis. Laboratories choose methods that are best suited for the geographical area that they service. Most labs will offer different methods upon request to accommodate most customers; you will have to know what to request first. Sending the same sample to several labs for comparison will be quite confusing unless you do your homework to determine what methods are used. I have talked with several customers after they have submitted the same sample to different labs without understanding the differences. They have been very unhappy and disappointed with the outcome.

Let's look at a good example of different methods—for example, phosphorus. There are nine phosphorus test methods that I am aware of. All of these methods were run on a specific soil sample and produced results anywhere from 10.5 to 656 ppm. If you know how to interpret the results for each of these tests, you should come up with the same recommendation. If you do not have the correct threshold levels for the method provided, you could make a big mistake in interpretation.

## Presentation of Data

What units of measure do you feel comfortable with? Do you prefer graphic results, high and low distinctions, or an actual value found?

Soil reports come in all shapes and sizes. Some reports are very colorful and show your results in a graphic form. Various reports show values as low, adequate or high. A number of reports show actual values found for each parameter. Reporting styles also vary regarding the reporting of desired levels, sufficiency levels, and base saturation percentages. What style are you most comfortable with? A combination of these styles may be most helpful.

Units of measure can vary from parts per million, pounds per acre, pounds per 1,000 square feet, or kilograms per hectare. It is very important that the laboratory is aware of your sampling depth if you will be receiving your results in a pound per acre or pound per 1,000 square feet format. The sampling depth will affect the value reported. It is vital to be aware of units when comparing reports from different laboratories. You have to compare apples to apples. Looking at a phosphorus example again will explain this. A laboratory may report phosphorus at 50 ppm P and another may report it at 229 pounds per acre $P_2O_5$. These two results are the same; however the units are the difference.

Does the soil report offer a recommendation? Where did it come from? Some recommendations are generic computer recommendations that give a ballpark range for optimum levels of nutrients. These may or may not be for a specific geographical area. If you are growing a unique or exotic crop, then you may need some specific advice. Inquire about the services of an independent agronomist.

## Logistics

How do you get your sample to the lab? Most labs will provide a soil sample bag or suggest a suitable alternative. Soil laboratories receive hundreds of samples each day. Be sure to acquire the appropriate paper-work from the laboratory to submit with your sample. Incomplete information will only delay the processing of your samples. Packing your samples for shipment is very important. Be sure to pack the samples tightly in a box. Pack newspaper or other packing material around the samples to keep them from bouncing around in the box. If samples can move around during shipment, they sometimes break open and can be destroyed. Resampling will add to your cost in time and money.

How long will this process take? Turnaround time in the whole soil test-ing process is imperative. Laboratories understand that your test results can be time sensitive. Don't hesitate to contact the lab if you have an emer-gency situation and need "rush" service. To determine your approximate turnaround time, consider the time it takes to get the sample to the lab (two to three days) and perform the analysis (three to four days). Turnaround time varies from one lab to another and also varies by season. You may want to contact the lab to inquire about their current turnaround time.

How do you get your report? You do not want the report held up somewhere after you have already waited through shipping and testing procedures. Reports are usually emailed or made available on the Inter-net on the same day the testing is completed. Be sure your correct email address and/or a fax number is submitted with your samples to get your results as soon as possible.

This is just the tip of the iceberg when looking at differences in laborato-ries. Laboratory instrumentation is continually improving. More parameters can be detected in a short amount of time and detection limits keep getting smaller. More efficient and "green" procedures are always being investi-gated. Embrace the advancements. Visionaries like Dr. Albrecht are still being cited in soil analysis circles. If he was continuing his research today, I believe he would embrace the latest technology and tools available.

So, the question still looms . . . which laboratory is best for you? Take the time to do your homework. It will be worth the investment and you will receive the value that you expect. Explore laboratory websites, call a lab and ask some questions, ask your friends about their experiences. Make sure you acquire the appropriate paperwork and instructions from the lab that you choose. When you have selected a laboratory that meets your needs and you are comfortable, stick with it. Jumping from lab to lab will only discourage you on your quest to improving soil fertility.

*Susan Shaner is the founder and a director of Logan Labs in Lakeview, Ohio.*
*Originally printed in Acres U.S.A. October 2011 issue.*

## Which extracting method is best?

Among all the soil testing laboratories, you will undoubtedly find many different extracting solutions and opinions about which is the best. The two most prevalent are Mehlich III and ammonium acetate, but there are also a lot of people using the Morgan and modified Morgan extracts. I feel that the best results for the standard soil tests are achieved from two extracting solutions—ammonium acetate and Mehlich III. I have used one or both of these extracting solutions exclusively for my entire consulting career. The soil testing industry as a whole, private and university labs alike, have settled on these two solutions.

The Mehlich III is rapidly becoming the extracting solution of choice. I believe this movement to the Mehlich III extracting method has been done not necessarily in the best interest of soil analysis but because it better suits soil testing laboratories. Mehlich III extracting solutions when coupled with inductively coupled plasma (ICP) units can measure all the major and minor elements necessary for plant growth at one time. Using the other extractants such as ammonium acetate will require additional extractions for phosphorus and the trace elements. The Morgan extraction uses sodium acetate and is set up for colorimetric interpretation. This interpretation is a visual review, which may be subject to more variability depending upon the consistency and training of the lab personnel performing the test.

The Mehlich extracting solution is certainly not perfect as it is a strong acid and does not work well on calcareous soils. I will explain this further in the interpretation of soil tests section. Data may also be affected from samples of freshly limed soils because of the strong acidic solution. As you can see, this testing isn't an absolutely perfect science when it comes to extracting from an extremely complex medium such as the soil. The best you can hope for is good repeatability from the laboratory. This means minimizing the human interpretations present with colorimetric testing and using labs that use high-tech ICP units and other technologies that give results that are data driven.

The paste test, although still in its infancy, uses water as its extracting solution. For soil this is the least intrusive method for removing and dissolving nutrients. This test will also be discussed in more detail later. But I have to say right here, the paste test by itself is not the total answer. The best strategy right now for interpreting soils includes using a standard test, which indicates nutrients that are potentially available, and a paste test that indicates nutrients in solution. These tests along with a tissue analysis are about as good as it gets.

## Deciding what amount of nutrients to apply?

Briefly, there will be more on deciding which nutrients to apply in the chapters on balancing. There is a table (Figure 4) that I find helpful in deciding how and what level of nutrients to apply to adjust soil nutrients. This table shows the means (mass flow, diffusion or interceptive root growth) by which nutrients are taken up through the roots. This table also shows, with the exception of copper and iron, that most nutrients are picked up out of the liquid solution by either mass flow or diffusion. The mass flow nutrients that are anions (negatively charged ion) are nitrogen (N), sulfur (S), boron (B) and molybdenum (Mo). The cations (positively charged ions) calcium (Ca) and magnesium (Mg) are more free to move in solution and travel longer distances whereas other nutrients such as phosphorus (P), potassium (K) and manganese (Mn) move very little in solution. The later nutrients typically move from areas of high concentration to low concentration, but can bond quite readily in clays and with other nutrients which reduces their mobility.

The other very critical factor to consider is how do most of the nutrients move within the plant once the roots have taken them up. Nutrients like calcium, boron and manganese travel primarily in the xylem or the water transport system of the plant. This is primarily in one direction and very dependent upon the evapotranspiration (ET) happening in the plant. Calcium, boron and manganese are necessary nutrients for root development—especially calcium as it needs to be in contact with the growing root. Nutrients such as potassium and phosphorus on the other hand can travel freely in the phloem. If these nutrients are only surface applied due to no-till practices, then they will become stratified and subject to uptake only as long as the roots are active in the surface.

Looking again at Figure 4, this table can also help with interpretation of plant tissue analysis. For example, plants that are short or deficient in copper may indicate a lack of this nutrient in the soil or a root development problem. This may be a physical structure, compaction, or another nutrient problem (such as calcium level affecting root growth). I have seen an almost fourfold increase in copper deficiencies found in soybeans over corn crops. This might be just the difference between the soybean taproots and the fibrous root system of corn plants. Personally I think a lot of the problem is related to compaction issues since many of our beans are no-till planted into corn stalks. Plants tend to grow at the rate provided by the least available nutrient. Compaction issues will almost always result in many other nutrient deficiencies (especially potassium and phosphorus). There will be more on identifying nutrient deficiencies using tissue analysis later in this book.

# Nutrient Uptake Methods Through the Roots

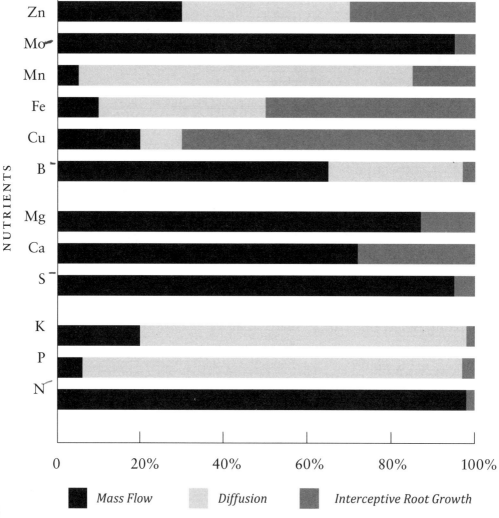

**Percentage of Nutrient Uptake Through Roots
by Mass Flow, Diffusion and Interceptive Root Growth**

**Fig. 4** *The percentage of nutrient uptake through the roots by mass flow,
diffusion and direct root interception. This table has been compiled from data
by Barber and Olsen (1968) and Dennis (1971).*

*Chapter 3*

# Balancing Nutrients on Low Exchange Capacity Soils

THIS CHAPTER WILL DEAL WITH THE TOPIC OF BALANCING SOILS THAT have a total exchange capacity of less than 10. This cutoff number is somewhat arbitrary, but it was chosen so that this chapter generally will deal with sandy soils. This would include artificially created soils used in golf course greens and tees, landscape and garden soils, as well as naturally occurring agricultural soils. Clay soils in the southern part of the United States where they are mostly kaolinite types that have been highly weathered and have low exchange could also be included in this section.

Looking at a soil, it is not as easy as you might think to decide if the soil falls into this low exchange capacity classification. The total exchange capacity (TEC) or cation exchange capacity (CEC) as they appear on a standard soil test are the result of the summation of cations collected from the extracting solution. The main difference between TEC and CEC is basically that the TEC measures the sodium cations and the CEC does not. The assumption is that all these cations are extracted from the soil colloid. This may or may not be the case. Some of these cations could be the result of soil fertilizer being dissolved or lime breaking down in the extracting solutions.

Be warned that the low pH extracting solution method such as used by Mehlich III is capable of dissolving lime-based or calcareous sands and exaggerating the exchange capacity. The exchange capacities shown in Figure 5 would rival a muck soil or one of the heaviest clay soils in the country, not a golf course green. An extracting solution that is pH neutral such as ammonium acetate will not dissolve the lime in soils so dramatically, however numbers may still be exaggerated.

There is only one way to find out the exact exchange capacity of your soil. This is done in the laboratory by saturating the soil sample with sodium, barium or ammonium and then flushing the sample with an alcohol to remove any cations not attached to the soil colloids. The above-mentioned cations contained in the saturated soil are then removed from the soil colloids by the extracting solution. The amount of cations, which are attached to the colloids, will produce the actual exchange capacity. Most people who have worked with their land for any length of time can tell if their standard soil tests have exaggerated exchange capacities.

Exaggerated exchange capacities that are the result of dissolving lime in the soil do not normally affect the extraction of other cations and trace elements. The problem arises when labs set recommended or desired levels for cations based on the exchange capacity. For example the desired amounts of potassium and magnesium could be overstated as shown by the soils in Figure 4. Anytime that the pH is much above 7, except when it is the result of sodium levels, the exchange capacities could be elevated. It is for these reasons that I find little benefit in using the standard test on calcareous sands—especially when using low pH extracting solutions. The paste test, which will be covered later in detail, is my choice for analysis in these situations.

# Comparing Golf Greens on Calcareous Soil

| | | Green | Green | Green |
|---|---|---|---|---|
| Sample Location | | Green | Green | Green |
| Sample ID | | 1 | 4 | 6 |
| Lab Number | | 40 | 41 | 42 |
| Sample Depth (inches) | | 6 | 6 | 6 |
| Total Exchange Capacity (m.e.) | | 31.29 | 34.49 | 33.28 |
| pH of Soil Sample | | 8.00 | 8.00 | 8.00 |
| Organic Matter (percent) | | 2.12 | 2.50 | 2.26 |
| **Anions** SULFUR: p.p.m. | | 16 | 15 | 15 |
| Mehlich III Phosphorus: as ($P_2O_5$) lbs. / acre | | 81 | 97 | 90 |
| **Exchangeable Cations** CALCIUM: lbs. / acre | Desired Value | 8510 | 9381 | 9053 |
| | Value Found | 11457 | 12683 | 12230 |
| | Deficit | | | |
| MAGNESIUM: lbs. / acre | Desired Value | 901 | 993 | 958 |
| | Value Found | 308 | 323 | 306 |
| | Deficit | -593 | -670 | -652 |
| POTASSIUM: lbs. / acre | Desired Value | 976 | 1076 | 1038 |
| | Value Found | 132 | 125 | 132 |
| | Deficit | -844 | -951 | -906 |
| SODIUM: lbs. / acre | | 60 | 50 | 62 |
| **Base Saturation %** Calcium (60 to 70%) | | 91.55 | 91.93 | 91.86 |
| Magnesium (10 to 20%) | | 4.10 | 3.90 | 3.83 |
| Potassium (2 to 5%) | | 0.54 | 0.46 | 0.51 |
| Sodium (0.5 to 3%) | | 0.41 | 0.31 | 0.41 |
| Other Bases (Variable) | | 3.40 | 3.40 | 3.40 |
| Exchangeable Hydrogen (10 to 15%) | | 0.00 | 0.00 | 0.00 |
| **Trace Elements** Boron (ppm) | | 0.53 | 0.5 | 0.52 |
| Iron (ppm) | | 103 | 141 | 118 |
| Manganese (ppm) | | 61 | 68 | 56 |
| Copper (ppm) | | 1.73 | 1.78 | 1.67 |
| Zinc (ppm) | | 5.33 | 4.91 | 4.74 |
| Aluminum (ppm) | | 28 | 75 | 36 |

**Fig. 5** *A comparison of three golf greens on calcareous soil showing results from samples taken at 6 inch depths. Results show the desired levels.*

At the other end of the pH scale, exchange capacities may also be elevated due to a high concentration of hydrogen cations. Exchange capacities are measured in milliequivalents (mEq). Without getting into the specifics here, it is widely accepted that . . .

> 1.0 mEq of hydrogen = 20 pounds of hydrogen in an acre furrow slice (AFS)
>
> 1.0 mEq of calcium = 400 pounds of calcium in an acre furrow slice
>
> 1.0 mEq of magnesium = 240 pounds of magnesium in an acre furrow slice
>
> 1.0 mEq of potassium = 780 pounds of potassium in an acre furrow slice
>
> 1.0 mEq of sodium = 460 pounds of sodium in an acre furrow slice

When you look at the above numbers, it is easy to see that when adjusting the balance in the soil, the milliequivalents (mEq) of the exchange capacity will constantly be changing. By replacing a *single* positively charged hydrogen cation on the colloid with a *double* positively charged cation of calcium, the exchange capacity is going to go down. The colloidal charge of the soil is basically fixed and the overall electrical balance will be maintained at the expense of the number of cations found in solution. As plants take up nutrients such as calcium and magnesium, the plant exchanges hydrogen ions in order to maintain an electrical balance in both the plant as well as the soil. Figure 6 is a comparison of the same field before and after liming has occurred. Notice the drop in the exchange capacity from one year to the next year. This was primarily due to the lime that was applied during the fall of 2006. The amount of calcium and magnesium applied was doubled (an increase of 5,394 to 10,647 lbs. of calcium and 506 to 1,277 lbs. of magnesium) but the total exchange capacity (TEC) went down because of the amount of exchangeable hydrogen that was lost. Exchange capacities are not static and should fluctuate as soils balance. If you notice that the exchange varies on your test results, first take note of any change in the cation amounts and then the pH values.

Clay and organic matter provide the bulk of the exchange sites that are used for holding cations. Pure vermiculite-type clay can contribute upwards of 150 CEC mEq per 100 grams whereas kaolinite clay has a CEC around 5 mEq per 100 grams. Humus, depending upon its quality, can contribute from 100 to >300 mEq per 100 grams of CEC.

# Two Soil Results Before and After Applying Lime

| Sample Location | | LS-5 | LS-5 |
|---|---|---|---|
| Sample ID | | 2006 | 2007 |
| Lab Number | | 38 | 109 |
| Sample Depth (inches) | | 9 | 9 |
| Total Exchange Capacity (m.e.) | | 42.12 | 36.04 |
| pH of Soil Sample | | 4.00 | 5.40 |
| Organic Matter (percent) | | 59.39 | 40.92 |
| Anions | **SULFUR:** p.p.m. | 40 | 81 |
| | **Mehlich III Phosphorus:** as ($P_2O_5$) lbs. / acre | 364 | 422 |
| Exchangeable Cations | **CALCIUM:** lbs. / acre     Value Found | 5394 | 10647 |
| | **MAGNESIUM:** lbs. / acre     Value Found | 506 | 1277 |
| | **POTASSIUM:** lbs. / acre     Value Found | 387 | 495 |
| | **SODIUM:** lbs / acre | 39 | 39 |
| Base Saturation % | Calcium (60 to 70%) | 21.34 | 49.23 |
| | Magnesium (10 to 20%) | 3.34 | 9.84 |
| | Potassium (2 to 5%) | 0.79 | 1.17 |
| | Sodium (0.5 to 3%) | 0.14 | 0.15 |
| | Other Bases (Variable) | 9.40 | 6.60 |
| | Exchangeable Hydrogen (10 to 15%) | 65.00 | 33.00 |
| Trace Elements | Boron (ppm) | 0.35 | 0.75 |
| | Iron (ppm) | 513 | 524 |
| | Manganese (ppm) | 14 | 14 |
| | Copper (ppm) | 0.23 | 1.45 |
| | Zinc (ppm) | 3.49 | 3.54 |
| | Aluminum (ppm) | 828 | 951 |

**Fig. 6** *A two-year comparison of the same field before and after lime was applied.*

Before balancing soil nutrient levels, it is important to understand the nature of the soil samples collected and realize the potential ramifications of nutrient stratification. Assuming that the sample was consistently collected at a 6 inch depth, it is imperative that we keep in mind that the results from the lab will represent a sample that is a composite of all the layers from the surface down to that 6 inch depth. Figure 2 shows how different these layers can be within the core.

Just because the soil core composite visually looks good, doesn't mean that the plants are getting a sufficient level of nutrients. Nutrients such as phosphorus and potassium can move up or down readily in the phloem of the plant. However nutrients like calcium and boron move only in one direction through the xylem, or water transport system, of the plant. Consequently, the layers of soil where root activity is taking place will affect the overall nutrient level in the plant. Tissue analysis is the only way to find out from the plant whether the nutrients are balanced. When using tissue analysis we also may want to adjust our soil criteria as to what the best balance may be for our area.

---

## Guidelines for Low Total Exchange Capacity Soils

The starting guidelines (desired levels) for a standard soil report using the Mehlich III extraction solution (at 1 part soil to 10 parts extracting solution) are shown in Figure 16. Unless the soils being extracted are of a high pH (>7.2), ammonium acetate extractions will be close enough to the Mehlich extraction numbers that these guidelines should be a very good starting point for an interpretation. I must caution though that balancing these low TEC soils using the basic cation saturation ratios (BCSR) will not work and a strategic level of available nutrients (SLAN) approach is better. The best approach is to use a combination of BCSR and SLAN in conjunction with the paste analysis. The paste analysis method will be discussed in more detail later in this section.

## pH

Ideally I would like to see pH around 6.5 for most average soils. This is just a little higher than what I recommend for heavier soils. The pH level can swing quite dramatically in sandy soils because they lack a high buffering capacity. Maintaining a pH near 6.5 will provide the best opportunity for nutrient solubility, however keeping it there will be a constant battle. This is especially true if you are irrigating these soils with water that has a high pH and are not adjusting the pH of the irrigation water. In high rainfall areas the pH could drop very quickly because the rainwater pH itself can often be as low as 5.5. Also because rainwater is very pure, this means that many nutrients can easily be dissolved in the water and leached away.

## Organic Matter

I would truly like to see organic matter at 7-8%, but if soils have this high of an organic matter level the soil sample would not fall into the low TEC soils section. Remember that clay and organic matter (humus) provide most of the exchange sites for holding cations. An organic matter level of 2.5% or lower is probably the most realistic that can be found in the low TEC soils since these soils are typically sands or highly weathered clays.

Organic matter is tied to the life of the soil. It is home for much of the soil biological life and needs to be protected at all costs. Organic matter is also responsible for much of the water-holding capacity in the soil. Early in my consulting career I ran across an example that shows the importance of organic matter in relation to the water-holding capacity. Imagine two boxes of soil each weighing 100 pounds. The first box contains a soil that is 2% organic matter and the second box contains a soil that is 4.5% organic matter. The boxes are completely air-dried. How much water could we pour in each of the boxes before the water would run out? A test showed that approximately 45 pounds of water could be added to the 2% organic matter soil box, but almost 150 pounds of water could be added to the 4.5% organic matter soil box before the water started to run out. It is important to realize that the relationship of the water-holding capacity to organic matter content is not linear but logarithmic. A small increase in organic matter can have a huge increase in water-holding capacity, as well as an increase in the nutrient-holding capacity.

## Sulfur

Sulfur levels at 20-25 ppm should keep most plants out of a deficiency providing that nitrogen is adequate. Very seldom have I seen a sulfur deficiency in my tissue analysis except when nitrogen had become a limiting factor. If nitrogen were going to be held to a minimum (especially in turfgrass), I would advise keeping sulfur on the high side and closer to 25 ppm. See Figure 26 later in this book for a chart of how to use sulfur to lower pH levels.

## Phosphorus

I would like to see phosphorus levels at 250-300 lbs. per acre. This might seem like a high level, but phosphorus is so readily tied up by calcium and magnesium at the higher pH range and tied up by aluminum and iron at the low pH range that its availability to plants is very limited. I have seen levels approaching 1,000 lbs. per acre and even then a tissue analysis was coming back short. This is very prevalent in high pH soil situations. After collecting corn tissue analysis results for five years on my clients' farms, I found that 51% of the time, corn at pre-6 leaf collar phase was deficient in phosphorus, even though 95% had received a high phosphorus starter fertilizer two inches below and two inches off to the side (2 x 2) when the seed was planted.

During this corn nutrient study, I also collected ear leaf tissues on the same fields. I found a correlation between zinc and phosphorus levels in the ear leaf tissue samples. When zinc was adequate in the tissues, the phosphorus levels were much improved. Consequently I came to the conclusion that achieving a recommended or strategic soil nutrient level does not guarantee that the plant will get all the phosphorus or other nutrients that it needs. Phosphorus is probably the most difficult major element to make available for plant use.

The issues arising from nutrient availability could range from having low microbial activity for solubilization, another nutrient interfering with uptake, or even the total lack of a nutrient necessary for the transport of minerals from the root to the tissue.

## Calcium

When it comes to calcium and low TEC soils it is very difficult to achieve some sort of balance. Calcium should be set at 1,200 lbs. per acre as a minimum, however this is more calcium than a soil can hold on the colloid, especially for a TEC level that is less than 4. That means some calcium must be free-floating in the soil. This free calcium is quick to tie up phosphorus and boron.

Calcium for uptake needs to be at the root tips since it is primarily mobile in the plant through the xylem, the water transport system for the plant. This presents some interesting problems for this nutrient. Besides the fact that it has to be soluble and in close proximity to growing roots, movement of calcium up and into the plant is dependent upon evapotranspiration. When there are high humidity conditions and/or cloudy days, calcium movement in the plant is very limited. Sources for calcium are basically lime and gypsum. The lime comes in two types, dolomite and high calcium. Dolomite generally has a calcium level around 21% and around 12% magnesium. Alternatively the high calcium limes generally have calcium levels above 30% and less than 3% magnesium.

Lime-stabilized sludge—or the now politically correct term of biosolids—is also a source of calcium, but the calcium material in the product is highly reactive. The pH of this material is 12 when it comes out of the stabilization process. It should be used only as a source of lime and not for the nutrient content in the product. Biosolids should be incorporated into soils due to the potential of odor issues that could arise.

Selecting a lime, which satisfies the need for both calcium and magnesium, *should* be rather simple. The problem lies with the hundreds of different grinds, which affect the particle size and ulti-mately the solubility of the product. Applying a very fine lime would be the most predictable, however in low TEC soils small amounts would have to be used many times during the course of the season. This would be feasible for the turfgrass industry, but is not very practical for the general agricultural industry. Keep in mind that any source of calcium applied to the soil will react with phosphorus and precipitate it out of solution. Analyzing a limed soil with the paste test, which will be discussed later in this book, generally shows that the soluble phosphorus is reduced by half. Lime with a particle size of 60-80% passing a 100-mesh would be the best type for the agricultural sector.

The main problem with liming low TEC soil is the temptation to overlime and raise the pH above 6.5. When this happens the availability of phosphorus and many trace elements are reduced. Many of the low exchange capacity soils are in no-till situations and are subjected to stratification issues as seen in Figure 2.

Aggressive tillage such as plowing is the fastest way to fix the stratifi-cation issue found with lime use. This can be easily done in the general agriculture sector, but really should be best done following a wheat crop. After plowing, the ground should be worked down and a cover crop sown to prevent erosion. Many farmers are reluctant to perform such an aggressive tillage program due to governmental policies and pressure from regulatory agencies.

The turfgrass industry can deeply aerate and topdress with a balanced soil. Simply topdressing with sand and not adjusting the balance within the topdress material is truly a missed opportunity for improving fertility at deeper levels in the soil. Applying a calcium source immediately after core aeration will allow some of the calcium to get down to the bottom of the cores. As long as the pH is below 6.5, lime is the most economical way to add calcium and magnesium as well as to adjust the pH levels. However Figure 7 shows how difficult it is to impact a large portion of soil with just core aeration. Gypsum is a great source of soluble calcium but it will not adjust the pH as lime does.

## Comparing the Area of Impact for Various Core Aeration Methods

### Amount of Area Impacted For Various Coring Programs

| Core Space In. | Holes Per Sq. Ft. | Tine Dia. In. | Tine Depth In. | Area removed each pass | Number of passes with aerifyer to impact a given area of the field | | |
|---|---|---|---|---|---|---|---|
| | | | | | 50% Removed | 25% Removed | 10% Removed |
| 2 | 36 | 0.5 | 3/8 | 5% | 10 | 5 | 2 |
| | | 0.75 | 3/8 | 11% | 5 | 2 | 1 |
| 3 | 16 | 0.5 | 3/8 | 2.2% | 22 | 11 | 5 |
| **Ryan Lawnaire® 28** | | **0.75** | **3/8** | **5%** | **10** | **5** | **2** |
| 4 | 9 | 0.5 | 3/8 | 1.3% | 40 | 20 | 8 |
| **Ryan Lawnaire® IV& V, Lesco Drum Aerator** | | **0.75** | **3/8** | **3%** | **18** | **9** | **4** |
| 6 | 4 | 0.5 | 3/8 | 0.5% | 90 | 45 | 18 |
| | | 0.75 | 3/8 | 1.3% | 40 | 20 | 8 |
| 8 | 2.25 | 0.5 | 3/8 | 0.31% | 161 | 81 | 32 |
| | | 0.75 | 3/8 | 0.69% | 72 | 36 | 15 |

**Fig. 7** *Research from Iowa State University on the amount of area impacted by various core aeration programs.*

## Magnesium

Magnesium is a very important nutrient affecting processes like phosphorus utilization, chlorophyll and structural components. Much like calcium, it is hard to have enough magnesium on the soil colloid in very light soils. If the only test you can do on a low TEC soil is a standard test, I would set the strategic level for magnesium around 200 lbs. per acre and a base saturation at a 15-20% level. This base saturation level is about 5 points higher than I would recommend for a higher

TEC soil. In the heavier soils, magnesium excesses can lead to tighter, more compact soils. This is not generally the case in the sandier soils, so a higher base saturation, such as around 20%, is less likely to lead to physical issues.

## Potassium

Potassium is so critical for many plant functions such as disease resistance, carbohydrate production, and water utilization that deficiencies are a serious situation. Setting a strategic level of 260 lbs. per acre is still low for many crop production levels. On sandy soils many crops must rely on having a deep root development in order to find enough potassium. Figure 11 shows the crop nutrient requirements for corn, soybeans and wheat crops. Although a 180 bushel per acre corn crop only removes 48 lbs. of $K_2O$ each year, the corn crop must have an equivalent of 400 lbs. of potash to produce both the grain and stover. Therefore the corn roots must pull some potassium from outside the soil sampling zone. Looking at a five year corn tissue study (Figure 12) that I performed, it showed that potassium at the pre-6 leaf collar stage was deficient an average of 63% of the time. This number rose to over 90% by ear leaf sampling time. Certainly one could argue that roots are not fully developed enough to pick up potassium in the early stages of a plants life, but this explanation does not fully explain the issue that the corn ear leaf samples always increased and in such a big number of deficiencies compared to the early samples.

Another factor leading to some poor potassium results when using tissue data is the sharp increase in plant populations over the last few decades. Corn populations have grown from 24,000 in the early 1980s to more than 34,000 today. This is a density increase of nearly 42% in a little over three decades. The corn crops have not increased their removal of potassium all that much, but the amount needed to support plant growth has markedly increased.

Figure 11 shows that the corn stover at a yield rate of 180 bushel per acre requires 192 lbs. of $K_2O$ or about 325 lbs. of potash (0-0-60) per acre. This chart is well over 15 years old when the acceptable population for corn was 24,000-26,000 plants per acre. With the increase and the corn populations now almost 50% higher, the potassium on the chart should probably be raised 30-35% or 400-450 lbs. per acre.

On average, both soybean and wheat crops were deficient in potassium over 70% of the time. In addition the nature of northwest Ohio soils makes it very difficult to take up potassium. This is in part due to the types of clay and the level of compaction we consider acceptable for this region. The effect of moving to no-till and minimum tillage may be part of the reason for the poor performance in potassium uptake, especially among the wheat and soybean crops.

## Sodium

Sodium is quite important for carrots, barley, beets, wheat and ryegrass crops. Most crops however, show very little response to sodium. If sodium becomes too high it has the capacity to first block calcium uptake, but also to impact magnesium and potassium to a lesser degree. Having sodium levels between 20-40 lbs. on the standard test is a good number to use as a guideline. I have noticed that sodium levels at the 20-40 lb. level on the standard test may seem quite low however, if the calcium solubility is low on the paste test, the sodium will come through quite high. More will be discussed about this topic in the paste section in Chapter 5.

Sodium problems seem to be mostly confined to localize areas around bodies of saltwater and in areas where sodium is high in irrigation water. Also note that irrigation water may not be very high in sodium, but poor irrigation techniques such as watering small amounts many times (lightly and frequently) can quickly accumulate sodium in the root zone.

## Boron

Boron levels in the soil should range between 0.7 and 1.0 ppm. Obtaining these levels is not a guarantee that the plants will have all the boron they need. A five-year tissue study I did for corn, beans and wheat showed that boron was on average deficient 27% for corn, 15% for beans, and 82% for wheat. Boron travels primarily through the water transport system and consequently anything that reduces water flow through the plant such as high humidity, rain, cool temperatures and stagnant air will reduce boron translocation (movement). The tissues collected in my study were all taken early in plant life.

The growing conditions for winter wheat in Ohio just prior to jointing are generally cool and wet, which is probably the reason for such high deficiency levels in the tissue data.

————————

## Iron

Iron is a nutrient that I have not found to be a real problem in any of my soil consultations. Iron deficiencies can be induced with high pH levels or glyphosate applications. The light exchange capacity soils certainly have a high probability of having iron deficiencies—especially in the calcareous sands.

Since half of the iron taken up by plants is through interceptive root growth (Figure 4), developing a vigorous root system is critical to preventing iron deficiency. Applying iron as iron sulfate will have limited success unless a good root system is in place. Also a small amount of bicarbonates present in the soil can block uptake and induce iron deficiency.

Iron is not very mobile in the plant. This is why iron deficiency shows up first on the new growth. The deficiency symptoms are light yellow to white coloration and stunted growth. Consequently foliar feeding should not be just a one-time operation. Repeated applications of iron are necessary, especially if the deficiency occurs early in the growing season. Tissue testing is the best way to verify the deficiency, however any soil contamination on the leaf can result in high iron results and misinterpretation of the situation. Washing the tissues immediately after sampling them with distilled or bottle water will greatly reduce the possibility of contamination issues. A squirt bottle works well for large leaves; however samples such as grass clippings may need to be gently floated in a water bath and drained in a colander. Use a clean paper towel to lay the samples out until they are dry.

_____

## Manganese

Manganese levels in the soil measured by the standard soil test should range between 30 and 50 ppm. Even within that range there is no guarantee that the plants will be supplied adequate manganese. It is possible to have both manganese deficiency at 14 ppm with one soil as well as manganese toxicity at 14 ppm for another soil. The pH of the soil is a huge factor in determining manganese availability.

I found manganese toxicity with some muck soils when the pH was 4, but when the pH was increased to above 7 the availability came crashing down and the toxicity levels vanished. Manganese is picked up in the elemental reduced form, therefore conditions in the soil that favor oxidation reduce manganese availability. Loose, well aerated, high pH soils are almost certainly going to have manganese issues.

Research by Dr. Don Huber and others around the world have shown that glyphosate enhances manganese-oxidizing bacteria in the soil and this therefore reduces manganese uptake. According to Dr. Huber this issue is persistent over several years and not just a concern during the year that glyphosate was applied.

Manganese in soybeans affects the enzyme system to the point that it controls the uptake of almost every other nutrient. Figures 8 and 9 show the effect that manganese has on the uptake of other nutrients at different manganese levels. The numbers shown in bold are considered deficient. The magic number appears to be around 40 ppm of manganese. Once soybean tissues drop below this level many major and minor elements drop off. Figure 8 shows soybean tissue results taken from a low organic matter field (< 2.4% OM) while Figure 4 is tissue results taken from a field with higher organic matter field (4% OM).

## Soybean Tissue Analysis

| | N % | P % | K % | S % | Ca % | Mg % | B ppm | Fe ppm | Cu ppm | Mn ppm | Zn ppm |
|---|---|---|---|---|---|---|---|---|---|---|---|
| Field 1 | 5.94 | **0.26** | **1.69** | **0.24** | **0.66** | **0.26** | **26** | 70 | **5.2** | **28** | **19** |
| Field 1-E | 5.29 | **0.30** | **2.05** | 0.27 | **0.69** | **0.29** | **29** | 145 | **5.8** | **31** | **25.2** |
| Field 1-W | 5.54 | **0.37** | 2.65 | 0.33 | **0.95** | **0.34** | 43 | 106 | **7** | **36** | **31** |
| Field 1-EA | 6.49 | 0.38 | 2.43 | 0.42 | 0.88 | **0.29** | 51 | 114 | 11 | 50 | 41 |
| Field 1-WA | 6.57 | **0.37** | 2.40 | 0.44 | 0.90 | **0.27** | 53 | 117 | 12 | 46 | 44 |

**Fig. 8** *Soybean tissue analysis showing the level of manganese deficiency and how it affects the deficiency level of other elements. Samples from Field 1-EA and 1-WA were collected at pod set or R-2 stage while the other locations were collected at 3-4 trifoliate stage. With the exception of nitrogen and iron, notice how well the increase in manganese correlates to the increase of the other nutrients. Note that the figures in bold are considered deficient.*

| | N % | P % | K % | S % | Ca % | Mg % | B ppm | Fe ppm | Cu ppm | Mn ppm | Zn ppm |
|---|---|---|---|---|---|---|---|---|---|---|---|
| Field 7 Pre | 5.94 | **0.33** | **2.30** | 0.31 | **0.80** | **0.29** | **30** | **82** | **6.0** | **17** | **28** |
| Field 7 Post | 6.19 | **0.38** | 2.49 | 0.40 | **0.83** | **0.31** | 40 | 131 | 13 | 55 | 45 |

**Fig. 9** *Soybean tissue analysis at 4-5 trifoliate (pre-application) stage showing a manganese deficiency and at 6-7 trifoliate (post application) following a foliar application of only manganese carbonate. Note that the figures in bold are considered deficient.*

# Soil Test Guidelines
## for Low Exchange Capacity Soils (<10)

| | Desired Levels |
|---|---|
| Soil pH | 6.5 |
| Organic matter % | 2.5 |
| Sulfur   ppm | 20-25 |
| Mehlich III Phosphorus  lbs./ac. | 250 |
| | |
| Calcium  lbs./ac. | 1,800-2,500 |
| Magnesium  lbs./ac. | 200-360 |
| Potassium  lbs./ac. | 220-400 |
| Sodium  lbs./ac. | 20-40 |
| Base Saturation % | |
| Calcium % | 65 |
| Magnesium % | 15-18 |
| Potassium % | 5-7 |
| Sodium % | 0.5-1.0 |
| Exchangeable Hydrogen % | 10 |
| | |
| Boron ppm | 0.7-1.0 |
| Iron ppm | >50 |
| Manganese ppm | 25-30 |
| Copper ppm | 2.5-3.5 |
| Zinc ppm | 6-8 |
| Aluminum ppm | <600 |

**Fig. 10** *Soil test guidelines for low exchange capacity soils using the SLAN approach.*

## Nutrient Requirements for Corn, Beans and Wheat

| Crop/ Yield | Plant Part | Nutrients | | | | | | | | | | | |
|---|---|---|---|---|---|---|---|---|---|---|---|---|---|
| | | N | $P_2O_5$ | $K_2O$ | Mg | S | Ca | Cl | B | Cu | Fe | Mn | Zn |
| **Corn** 180 bu./ac. | Grain | 170 | 70 | 48 | 16 | 14 | 20 | 2.5 | .13 | .70 | .17 | .10 | .16 |
| | Stover | 70 | 30 | 192 | 34 | 16 | 34 | 1.5 | .06 | .06 | 1.0 | 1.7 | .33 |
| | Total | 240 | 100 | 240 | 50 | 30 | 54 | 4.0 | .19 | .76 | 1.7 | 1.8 | .49 |
| **Soy-beans** 60 bu./ac. | Grain | 252 | 49 | 87 | 17 | 12 | 12 | 3 | .08 | .07 | .71 | .08 | .07 |
| | Stover | 84 | 16 | 58 | 10 | 13 | 90 | – | – | .02* | 1.8* | .31* | .07* |
| | Total | 336 | 67 | 135 | 27 | 25 | 102 | | | .09 | 2.5 | .39 | .14 |
| **Wheat** 80 bu./ac. | Grain | 144 | 44 | 26 | 12 | 5 | 2.7 | 6.7 | .08 | .07 | .60 | .18 | .28 |
| | Stover | 42 | 10 | 135 | 12 | 15 | 12 | 26 | .03 | .03 | 2.6 | .32 | .11 |
| | Total | 186 | 54 | 161 | 24 | 20 | 14.7 | 32.7 | .11 | .10 | 3.2 | .50 | .39 |

*= based on 6,000 lbs. of soybean residue

**Fig. 11** *Nutrient Requirements per year for corn, beans and wheat with one projected yield.*

## Corn Tissue Results Showing Nutrient Deficiencies Over 5 Years

| | N % | P % | K % | S % | Ca % | Mg % | B ppm | Fe ppm | Cu ppm | Mn ppm | Zn ppm |
|---|---|---|---|---|---|---|---|---|---|---|---|
| **Desired Level** | 3.4 | 0.34 | 3.5 | 0.24 | 0.70 | 0.25 | 7.2 | 64.0 | 8.8 | 56.0 | 40.0 |
| % Deficient | | | | | | | | | | | |
| 2002 | 1 | 43 | 84 | 4 | 94 | 34 | 4 | 0 | 4 | 51 | 76 |
| 2003 | 2 | 28 | 89 | 2 | 80 | 74 | 11 | 0 | 6 | 42 | 87 |
| 2004 | 6 | 54 | 68 | 3 | 68 | 87 | 35 | 0 | 3 | 35 | 88 |
| 2005 | 13 | 59 | 56 | 24 | 43 | 44 | 23 | 0 | 27 | 74 | 86 |
| 2006 | 37 | 72 | 16 | 8 | 39 | 37 | 64 | 0 | 55 | 54 | 96 |
| Average | 11 | 51 | 63 | 8 | 65 | 55 | 27 | 0 | 19 | 51 | 87 |

**Fig. 12** *Corn tissue results taken for 5 straight years showing the percentage of the various nutrient deficiencies. Plants sampled at the pre-6 leaf collar stage.*

## Corn Ear Leaf Tissue Results Showing Nutrient Deficiencies over 3 Years

| | Nutrients | | | | | | | | | | |
|---|---|---|---|---|---|---|---|---|---|---|---|
| | N % | P % | K % | S % | Ca % | Mg % | B ppm | Fe ppm | Cu ppm | Mn ppm | Zn ppm |
| **Desired Level** | 3 | 0.28 | 2.21 | 0.23 | 0.60 | 0.20 | 6.6 | 50 | 7.7 | 44 | 33 |
| % Deficient | | | | | | | | | | | |
| 2004 | 22 | 56 | 89 | 33 | 0 | 50 | 11 | 0 | 0 | 39 | 67 |
| 2005 | 0 | 29 | 93 | 7 | 0 | 14 | 0 | 0 | 0 | 36 | 36 |
| 2006 | 20 | 100 | 93 | 73 | 60 | 33 | 87 | 0 | 33 | 53 | 100 |
| Average | 14 | 62 | 92 | 20 | 38 | 32 | 33 | 0 | 11 | 43 | 68 |

**Fig. 13** *Corn ear leaf tissue results taken for 3 years showing the percentage of various nutrient deficiencies.*

## Soybean Tissue Results Showing Nutrient Deficiencies Over 5 Years at Various Growth Stages

| | Nutrients | | | | | | | | | | |
|---|---|---|---|---|---|---|---|---|---|---|---|
| | N % | P % | K % | S % | Ca % | Mg % | B ppm | Fe ppm | Cu ppm | Mn ppm | Zn ppm |
| **Desired Level Pre-bloom** | 5.2 | 0.45 | 2.7 | 0.26 | 1.3 | 0.5 | 40 | 100 | 12 | 60 | 45 |
| **Desired Level Bloom** | 6 | 0.4 | 2.5 | 0.3 | 1.1 | 0.4 | 35 | 100 | 10 | 50 | 40 |
| 2002 % Deficient | 38 | 48 | 83 | 41 | 34 | 21 | 14 | 0 | 55 | 69 | 10 |
| 2003 % Deficient | 57 | 60 | 57 | 57 | 60 | 83 | 7 | 0 | 80 | 47 | 40 |
| 2004 % Deficient | 63 | 74 | 74 | 20 | 94 | 97 | 20 | 0 | 89 | 31 | 74 |
| 2005 % Deficient | 54 | 81 | 85 | 8 | 58 | 62 | 0 | 4 | 96 | 46 | 12 |
| 2006 % Deficient | 45 | 77 | 65 | 7 | 67 | 87 | 35 | 5 | 70 | 72 | 62 |
| Average | 51 | 68 | 73 | 27 | 63 | 70 | 15 | 2 | 76 | 53 | 40 |

**Fig. 14** *Soybean tissue results taken over 5 years showing the percentage of nutrient deficiencies present at the various growth stages. During 2002-2005 the tissue was collected early at the 3-5 trifoliate stage. Tissue samples for the year 2006 were collected later around the R-1 stage.*

## Wheat Tissue Results Showing Nutrient Deficiencies Over 5 Years at the Pre-Joint Stage

| | N % | P % | K % | S % | Ca % | Mg % | B ppm | Fe ppm | Cu ppm | Mn ppm | Zn ppm |
|---|---|---|---|---|---|---|---|---|---|---|---|
| **Desired Level** | 4.2 | 0.46 | 4.4 | 0.3 | 0.47 | 0.16 | 7 | 50 | 11 | 45 | 52 |
| 2002 % Deficient | 8 | 23 | 69 | 0 | 77 | 85 | 100 | 0 | 92 | 23 | 62 |
| 2003 % Deficient | 0 | 34 | 54 | 0 | 49 | 14 | 63 | 0 | 83 | 26 | 97 |
| 2004 % Deficient | 3 | 21 | 63 | 3 | 53 | 50 | 76 | 0 | 84 | 32 | 93 |
| 2005 % Deficient | 31 | 63 | 80 | 11 | 86 | 77 | 83 | 0 | 97 | 49 | 94 |
| 2006 % Deficient | 10 | 37 | 87 | 7 | 87 | 37 | 90 | 0 | 90 | 7 | 93 |
| Average | 10 | 36 | 71 | 4 | 70 | 53 | 82 | 0 | 89 | 27 | 88 |

**Fig. 15** *Wheat tissue results showing nutrient deficiencies from samples taken at the pre-joint stage over 5 years.*

## Paste Analysis

Low exchange capacity soils have a lot of issues when it comes to holding enough nutrients and maintaining colloidal balance. Sand with low organic matter is basically a soilless media. Since many of the nutrients required for crop production are not on the colloid, I find that the paste test is absolutely the best test for this situation. I also use the paste test along with the standard test on the higher exchange capacity soils. Since most of the nutrients taken up by plants are picked up by mass flow or diffusion (Figure 4) at the air/water interface near the plant roots, the paste test better correlates to tissue analysis than the standard test.

The paste test is done primarily by taking a large sample, approximately 200-400 grams of a composite soil mixture and saturating it with distilled water (or even better is to use clients' irrigation water) until it becomes a pancake batter consistency.

The sample is held in this "batter" state for 24 hours and then the water is vacuumed off. Similar to the standard test, the analysis is done on the extract. The level of nutrients that result from using a paste test is very small in comparison to a standard test. These levels will reflect what is equilibrating into solution from the colloid and all the undissolved minerals in the soil.

I have developed a set of desired levels based on crop response and hundreds of tissue analyses. Figure 16 shows the levels I use as my paste guidelines. This should be a starting point for someone located outside of northwest Ohio. Crop type, soil variations, compaction, your client's preferences, and the weather may all have an impact on your ideal desired nutrient levels.

Tissue samples at various critical times in the crop lifecycle will help you to adjust your levels up or down. Altering soil nutrient levels with fertilizer applications is easier in a low TEC soil since there is very little buffering capacity. These nutrient levels can also be quickly lowered due to crop uptake and water percolation through the profile. Paste tests should be repeated in-season—especially on soils with a TEC of < 5 in order to determine the rate of decline of the nutrient levels. Finding products with variable rates of solubility is important if in-season applications cannot be made. Even if in-season applications can be made, repeated paste testing is a good way to determine when the best time will be to make an application. This will not only reduce fertilizer expense but also cut down on the risk of overapplication.

## Understanding Solubility Testing

Just what is a soil paste or solubility test and when should you consider running the analysis? Solubility analysis is an attempt to see what is in the soil solution, or that which can readily go into solution off the colloid.

The diagram below is a conceptual picture of a root hair in the soil solution in proximity to a clay particle or soil colloid. The standard soil analysis measures the dots (nutrients) floating in solution as well as the dots (nutrients) held on the surface of the clay mineral, but not those trapped between the clay layers. In a standard soil test, the minerals attached to the surface of the clay particle are removed for analysis by using an extracting solution. A solubility analysis primarily looks at only the blue dots (nutrients) floating in solution.

It makes perfect sense to look at a test that measures nutrients only in solution when you study the research work done by Barber and Olsen in 1968 and Dennis in 1971. That research showed the bulk of the soil nutrients taken up by plants was through mass flow and diffusion from the soil solution. Very little nutrition enters the plants by the roots directly intercepting nutrients from the colloid or soil particles. So when should you use a solubility analysis? Those soils with exchange capacities less than 10 should be the first targeted for solubility analysis. This includes all sandy soils even calcareous sands, which tend to get exaggerated TECs on the standard soil test. It is nearly impossible to balance and hold that balance on low exchange capacity soils.

Since the holding capacity of low exchange soils is so small, plants grown on these soils primarily get their nutrition from applied nutrients with variable degrees of solubility. Solubility analysis will take you to a whole new level of understanding the relationship of soil and plant nutrition. When combined with the standard soil test and plant analysis you will get a much clearer picture of what soil nutrition means.

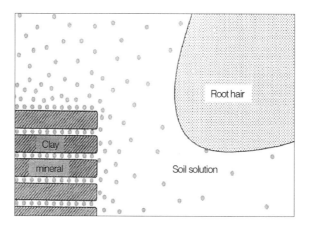

*The Soil Probe Newsletter, Logan Labs*

## Making Paste Analysis Recommendations

Making recommendations from a paste analysis incorporates both the SLAN approach and the BCSR approach. First, it is critical to meet the minimum strategic nutrient levels for growth and reproduction (Figure 16). Secondly, the nutrients in solution should be kept in balance to minimize interference issues. Even if all the strategic levels have been met, if a nutrient such as potassium is two or three times higher than the desired level, other cations such as calcium and magnesium should be elevated in order to maintain a balance. The type of crop and the level on the standard test would help make that determination. For crops such as corn or alfalfa that require a lot of potassium if the standard test does not show good levels of potassium, I would probably let the level stand and not elevate the calcium and magnesium. When raising levels to just balance out one nutrient, care must be taken not to create a salt issue. If the nutrient in excess is sodium and irrigation is available, flushing the soil may be the best solution. Most of the sodium issues that I see are created by irrigation practices. Irrigating with poor quality water or using poorly designed irrigation systems may result in the accumulation of sodium and/or bicarbonates. We will look at some of these in the soil test interpretation section in Chapter 5.

# Strategic Nutrient Level Paste Guidelines for Low Exchange Soils (TEC <10)

|  | Desired Levels |
|---|---|
| Soil pH | 6.2-6.5 |
| Soluble Salts ppm | <1,000 |
| Anions | |
| Sulfur ppm | 1-3 |
| Chlorides ppm | <60 |
| Bicarbonates ppm | <90 |
| Phosphorus ppm | 0.3-0.6 |
| Cations | |
| Calcium ppm | 30-40 |
| Magnesium ppm | 6-8 |
| Potassium ppm | 12-15 |
| Sodium ppm | <6 |
| Solution % | |
| Calcium % | 60 |
| Magnesium % | 20 |
| Potassium % | 12-15 |
| Sodium % | <5 |
| Trace Elements | |
| Boron ppm | 0.05-0.10 |
| Iron ppm | 0.5-1.5 |
| Manganese ppm | 0.07-0.15 |
| Copper ppm | 0.05-0.08 |
| Zinc ppm | 0.07-0.15 |
| Aluminum ppm | <15 |

**Fig. 16** *Optimum strategic nutrient levels and a solution balance guideline for paste tests.*

## Discussion of Paste Guidelines

The guidelines for the paste test shown on Figure 16 are just that —guidelines. I cannot emphasize enough that everyone needs to adjust these numbers based on their own crop tissue analysis and the subsequent crop response. There is one unknown factor that we face when using paste numbers and this is what I call the "flow rate into solution." See Figure 17 below.

## The Flow Rate in Solution Factor

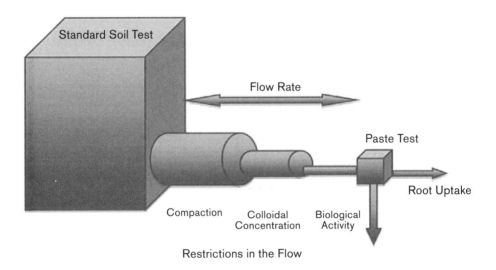

Fig. 17 *This diagram shows some of the many factors that affect flow rate and paste test results. The standard test gives the nutrient rate that is primarily held on the soil colloid whereas the paste test shows the level of nutrients readily available for root uptake and in solution form.*

The standard test reflects the large portion of nutrients primarily held on the soil colloid. These nutrients continually go back and forth into solution when they can be measured by the paste test. There are many factors that can affect the rate of exchange that allow nutrients to get into solution. The concentration of nutrients in the soil, compaction, biological activity, and moisture level are just a few factors that affect the flow rate of exchange into solution. With a standard test we know the level of nutrients in the soil. We cannot fully know though what restrictors may be present preventing nutrients from going into solution and being available to the plants. Therefore when plants pull nutrients out of solution we cannot be sure how fast they will be replaced. The replacement of nutrients may be adequate most of the time, but it is not known if they will be adequate during critical phases in the plant's life cycle. The only way to be sure of this is to tissue sample during those critical times. If the tissue analysis frequently comes up short, then raising the desired paste levels may be one way to overcome this problem. Increasing the paste test threshold levels simply means increasing a nutrient solubility by using a soluble fertilizer in a soil application. This can be accomplished in a number of ways. Nutrients which are easily tied up in the soil, such as phosphorus, can be banded or put down in a row application. The easiest, but not the cheapest, method is elevating the overall soil nutrient levels with buildup applications. Foliar feeding could be used if the deficiency is a short-term problem such as the result of adverse weather conditions. Certainly the wisest course of action is to remove as many of the factors that are restricting root mass development and hindering biological activity. Issues of compaction and nutrient stratification are the top concerns that can be mechanically removed through tillage or aeration. We are now learning from people like Dr. Huber, retired from Purdue University, that herbicide programs consisting of glyphosate have a negative impact on nutrient uptake. Changing or rotating our chemical program will help alleviate some of these added stresses.

## Nutrient Discussions

### Sulfur

Sulfur is one of the easiest elements to adjust when using the paste test since many sources are readily available. Ammonium sulfate will easily supply enough sulfur for crops requiring nitrogen. Potassium sulfate and K-Mag (potassium, magnesium and sulfur) are excellent soluble sources of sulfur. Gypsum is also a great source of sulfur. Keep in mind that high levels of sulfur in the soil when not as a result of one of the above mentioned applications could be an indication of poor soil drainage.

### Chloride

Although chlorides have been shown to have some nutritional value in small amounts, the real problem seems to be an excess of chloride accumulation from either irrigation or fertilizer applications. Figure 18 shows a chloride toxicity problem on sandy soil in no-till soybeans. The problem didn't show up until after the rain stopped. It was a result of improper spreading of a potassium chloride (muriate of potash) fertilizer.

## Chloride Damage on No-Till Soybeans

**Fig. 18** *Chloride damage shown on a no-till soybean field as a result of improper fertilizer application. Note the light and dark banding. The damage did not appear until the rain stopped.*

## Bicarbonates

Bicarbonate is a problem found on soils with an alkaline pH level over 7. Bicarbonate is frequently found in well water that has been pumped from limestone strata. Bicarbonate is a product of limestone disassociation and basically is the reason why liming soil raises the pH level. Bicarbonate, similarly to aluminum, does not have any nutritional benefits. High levels of bicarbonate constituents in the soil result in more of an interference issue. Excessive levels of bicarbonate from saturated calcareous soils or applied through the irrigation system can result in inducing iron chlorosis. As soils with high levels of bicarbonates dry down, calcium carbonate can precipitate out and consequently react with phosphorus. The phosphorus will precipitate out into a form of low solubility rock phosphate. Keeping the bicarbonates below 60-90 ppm should be adequate to keep the interferences to a minimum.

## Phosphorus

Phosphorus is one of the most difficult of the major nutrients to maintain solubility. It reacts with almost any cation (such as calcium, magnesium, zinc, iron, manganese and aluminum). Phosphorus bonds at low pH levels with iron, aluminum and bonds with calcium and magnesium at high pH levels. A pH level around 6.2-6.4 is critical for optimizing chances of maintaining phosphorus solubility. It is important to keep the standard soil test phosphorus levels on the high side around the 250 lbs. per acre mark. I have seen phosphorus levels on the standard test well over 1,000 lbs. per acre but because of high soil pH and cation interference the soluble phosphorus fell below the detection limit. The lighter soils are easier to achieve the 0.3-0.6 ppm solubility level, mainly because there are fewer nutrients challenging each other when bonding up.

Applications of any calcium source will tend to cut the soluble phosphorus numbers by half. The detection limits for phosphorus at Logan Labs is 0.1 ppm, so in most cases growers are always flirting with very small numbers of available phosphorus.

I prefer to make my lime or gypsum applications ahead of corn planting for two reasons. First, the high levels of calcium helps the fibrous root system and stalk quality and secondly most of my clients use row starter fertilizers so I can concentrate some phosphorus in the starter fertilizer and maintaining better availability for the corn.

Almost all of the commercial fertilizers, such as 18-46-0 (dry), 11-52-0 (dry), 10-34-0 (liquid) and the myriad of combinations are soluble forms of fertilizer, will boost the numbers on the paste test. Manure applications will directly and indirectly boost the soluble numbers on the paste test.

Indirectly, some of the solubility increase comes from organic acids produced from the manure, which leads to solubilizing of some of the existing soil phosphorus. Some livestock feeding programs contain the enzyme phytase, which improves the phosphorus availability in corn, normally bound up by phytin (a calcium magnesium salt of phytic acid).

Manures will directly increase phosphorus levels in the soil depending upon the content in the manure. Rations using a high level of corn, like those fed to chicken and swine, will contain higher levels of phosphorus compared to those levels found in dairy and horse manure. Whenever possible I prefer manures or composted manure because of the fact that they have a slow release of nitrogen, phosphorus and other nutrients as well as having the benefit of organic constituents.

## Calcium

Calcium solubility was something that I did not concern myself with early on in my consulting career. I had thought that if the base saturation level was around 65% calcium and 15% magnesium, there was not much more anyone could do. I was absolutely wrong in thinking this way. Two events prompted me to totally re-evaluate my position on this subject. The first was a chart I saw in the Alltech Biotechnology newsletter (Figure 19) that speaks volumes about the change in calcium solubility. Soil pH values and liming attitudes probably have changed very little from 1963 through 1999 but obviously, something in the soil has changed. In fact oranges were the only crop on this list that changed very little. If the analyzed oranges were from Florida, most would have been grown on calcium silicate or coral-based soils which are very high in calcium.

# Nutrient Values for Market Vegetable Crops

| Produce | Ca | | Mg | | K | |
|---|---|---|---|---|---|---|
| | 1963 | 1999 | 1963 | 1999 | 1963 | 1999 |
| Beans, raw | 56 | 37 | 32 | 25 | 243 | 209 |
| Broccoli, raw | 103 | 48 | 24 | 25 | 382 | 325 |
| Carrots, raw | 37 | 27 | 23 | 15 | 341 | 323 |
| Oranges, raw | 41 | 40 | 11 | 10 | 200 | 181 |
| Peaches, raw | 9 | 5 | 10 | 7 | 202 | 197 |
| Tomatoes, raw | 13 | 5 | 14 | 11 | 244 | 222 |

**Fig. 19** *Nutritional values showing changes in calcium, magnesium and potassium levels in various market vegetable crops after 36 years (comparing 1963 to 1999 harvests). Results are shown in mg/100g.*

The second eye-opening moment concerning calcium was triggered by a call from Gene, a potato grower in northwest Ohio who had been a client for over 20 years. He asked me to look at a field of potatoes that contained 30 feet of great looking potatoes and right next to this 30 feet of terrible looking potatoes (Figure 20). He said that the contrast was very prevalent on the sand hills. I drove up the next day and looked at the field. It was exactly as he had described it. The bad plants looked small, chlorotic, and had suffered necrosis on the leaf edges and on the new growth. I told Gene that it was definitely a nutrition problem and that I would collect soil samples from the good and bad areas and tell him by the end of the week what the problem was. I collected the samples and sent them off to the lab for a standard soil test analysis. Two days later the report came back and to my surprise the numbers for the good and bad soil samples looked almost identical (Figure 21).

## Potato Field Showing Both
## High and Low Exchange Capacity Soils

**Fig. 20** *A field of potatoes with strips of bad and good quality potato plants. In the foreground, the soil has better organic matter and a higher exchange capacity. Consequently this soil is more buffered and slower to respond to seasonal and nutritional stresses. The sand ridges in the middle of the picture have a low buffering capacity and a calcium solubility issue—this is the first area in the field to show stresses. If no nutritional corrections are done on the foreground soil, this area will eventually end up looking like the sand. The lighter exchange capacity of the sandy soil affects calcium solubility, which is compounded by the coarser soil resulting in less water to help dissolve the lime. Consequently it will need a finer grade of lime applied—but not too much at any one time.*

The numbers for the two soil samples were so close that had I not taken the samples, I would have thought that someone had taken one sample, split it in half and ran the test twice. I was stunned that the plants could look so different and yet the soil test results looked so similar. I didn't want to have to tell Gene that I didn't know what the problem was with the soil, so I looked for an alternative test. I remembered earlier in the year I had done some work for a greenhouse and used a paste test. The potatoes were being grown in a sandy soil, which is somewhat like a greenhouse soilless media, so I decided I would run a paste test. I immediately identified the problem with the soil (Figure 22). The solubility of calcium was 30.9 ppm in the soils where there were good potatoes, but only 10.7 ppm in the soil where there were bad potatoes. The previous fall Gene and I had noticed how low the pH had dropped in the field, but since it was going to be planted in potatoes the next spring, we didn't want to apply a full complement of lime and risk the chance of potato scab. So only 1,000 lbs. of lime was applied to the field that fall. As the lime was being applied though, the finer particles fell out right behind the truck and the coarser material was thrown further away, hence explaining the difference in calcium solubility and potato growth.

# Potato Growth Issues in NW Ohio Field
## Standard Soil Test Result

| | | | D-8A | | D-8A |
|---|---|---|---|---|---|
| Sample Location | | | D-8A | | D-8A |
| Sample ID | | | Poor | | Good |
| Lab Number | | | 466 | | 467 |
| Sample Depth (inches) | | | 9 | | 9 |
| Total Exchange Capacity (m.e.) | | | 5.56 | | 6.57 |
| pH of Soil Sample | | | 4.7 | | 4.5 |
| Organic Matter (percent) | | | 1.0 | | 1.6 |
| Anions | SULFUR: | p.p.m. | 111 | | 107 |
| | Mehlich III Phosphorus: | as ($P_2O_5$) lbs. / acre | 985 | | 997 |
| Exchangeable Cations | CALCIUM: lbs. / acre | Desired Value / Value Found / Deficit | 486 | | 518 |
| | MAGNESIUM: lbs. / acre | Desired Value / Value Found / Deficit | 110 | | 114 |
| | POTASSIUM: lbs. / acre | Desired Value / Value Found / Deficit | 382 | | 416 |
| | SODIUM: | lbs. / acre | 54 | | 46 |
| Base Saturation % | Calcium (60 to 70%) | | 21.85 | | 19.7 |
| | Magnesium (10 to 20%) | | 8.24 | | 7.23 |
| | Potassium (2 to 5%) | | 8.81 | | 8.12 |
| | Sodium (0.5 to 3%) | | 2.11 | | 1.52 |
| | Other Bases (Variable) | | 8.00 | | 8.40 |
| | Exchangeable Hydrogen (10 to 15%) | | 51.00 | | 55.0 |

**Fig. 21** *Soil report from the potato field showing almost similar results for the good (left) and bad (right) plant growth samples.*

When the standard test was used with the Mehlich extracting solution (which has a pH of 2.5), the solution was able to dissolve the coarser lime particles and consequently make the good and bad potato areas look the same on the results paper. It was these results that convinced me to start to look at all Gene's soils with the paste analysis. Later that fall, after I had run split/duplicate samples on every field analyzing the soil using both paste and standard analysis, I had asked Gene to pick out the three worst and three best fields based on his last five years of production. His results are listed in Figure 23. The first three fields (L-2C, L-3A, and K-1B) were his best and the last three (W-1A, W-2A, W-2B) were his worst. I was a little surprised because when I looked at just the standard test results, Gene's worst fields were the ones that I considered to be very balanced.

The field identified as L-2C, with a base saturation of 32.6% calcium was one of Gene's best. However, after looking at the paste test it was very obvious that I had to dig deeper and find out what was really happening here. I thought it very interesting that the good area of field D-8 (Figure 22) also performed the best when the calcium level was around 30-40 ppm. Through the use of paste testing and changing the solubility of the calcium by using gypsum, we were able to move the W farm from one of his worst producing fields (W-1A, W-2A, W-2B) to one of his best in just two years time.

Economically, calcium solubility can be changed most readily by using gypsum (calcium sulfate). Gypsum is not a lime, and it will not change the soil pH. Most of my applications vary between 800-1,200 lbs. per acre for the agricultural sector since that is about the minimum that can be bulk spread with a lime truck. For turfgrass, on the other hand, I should be able to get down to 8-10 lbs. per 1,000 square feet and make multiple applications if necessary. Mined gypsum as well as recycled wallboard has worked very well as a source for my clients. The recycled scrubbed gypsum from powerplants and wallboard contains the same calcium as the mined gypsum. This does not mean that high calcium limes should be ignored. If the pH drops below our ideal of 6.2, then use a very fine, high calcium lime which will pass 60-80% through a 100-mesh screen. Providing the high calcium lime is incorporated adequately, it will contribute to the calcium solubility. Unincorporated on the surface, the pH will then rise in that layer to around 7 and the solubility will drop off minimizing the effect of liming.

# Initial Solubility Comparisons
# of the Good and Bad Potato Sample Rows

| Lab Number | 192 | | 193 | |
|---|---|---|---|---|
| Description | D-8A Poor | Percentage in Solution | D-8 Good | Percentage in Solution |
| pH | 3.9 | | 4.3 | |
| Soluble Salts | 397 | | 397 | |
| Chloride | 41 | | 41 | |
| Nitrate NO3-N | 7.1 | | 11.3 | |
| Bicarbonate | 49.1 | | 45.4 | |
| | | | | |
| Sulfur | 48.7 | | 49.8 | |
| Phosphorus | 0.48 | | 0.38 | |
| Calcium | 10.7 | 16.9 | 30.9 | 34.3 |
| Magnesium | 5.8 | 15.1 | 12.2 | 22.5 |
| Potassium | 70.7 | 57.0 | 62.0 | 35.3 |
| Sodium | 8.0 | 11.0 | 8.1 | 7.8 |
| | | | | |
| Boron | 0.10 | | 0.14 | |
| Iron | 0.76 | | 0.65 | |
| Manganese | 1.82 | | 1.66 | |
| Copper | 0.04 | | 0.04 | |
| Zinc | 0.25 | | 0.25 | |
| Aluminum | 2.54 | | 1.90 | |
| Ammonia | 20.3 | | 12.20 | |

**Fig. 22** *This chart shows a comparison of the nutrient solubility between the good and bad potato row soil sample results before any amendments were added. Samples taken June 2, 1998.*

The calcium solubility threshold should range between 30 and 40 ppm providing that the potassium and magnesium levels are in line. I prefer to see a 5 to 1 calcium to magnesium ppm ratio value. This will result in a cation saturation with a 3 to 1 ratio or percentage values close to the ideal levels of 60% calcium and 20% magnesium. It might be hard to get the 60% calcium and 20% magnesium levels if the sodium or potassium is very high. The high solubility of nutrients such as sodium and potassium will tend to be higher than normal if the calcium threshold is not close to the 30-40 ppm level. In situations where sodium is high and the calcium meets the threshold levels of 30-40 ppm, you will have to push up the threshold level of calcium in order to obtain the 60% calcium and 20% magnesium balance. Also when trying to offset a sodium imbalance, be careful not to create a subsequent salt toxicity issue by exceeding the 1,000 ppm maximum salt concentration threshold.

## Calcium Comparisons on the Good and Bad Potato Fields—Mehlich III vs. Paste Test

| Field | Mehlich III ppm /% BS | pH 1:1 | Paste ppm /% BS | pH |
|-------|-----------------------|--------|-----------------|-----|
| L-2C | 502 / 32.6% | 5.0 | 38.2 /46.4 | 6.1 |
| L-3A | 1190 /59.4 | 6.2 | 37.1 /49.1 | 6.2 |
| K-1B | 1599 /60.1 | 6.1 | 28.2 /43.5 | 6.3 |
| W-1A | 868 /59.9 | 6.2 | 7.2 /35.9 | 6.1 |
| W-2A | 988 /63.2 | 6.1 | 5.7 /32.0 | 6.2 |
| W-2B | 1325 /65.2 | 6.5 | 5.8 /31.1 | 6.4 |

**Fig. 23** *A chart showing the comparison in calcium nutrient levels when using the standard test and paste test for duplicate samples in an Ohio potato farm.*

## Magnesium

Ideally, magnesium should be between 6-8 ppm in solution. It is hard to speak about magnesium by itself when we are working to achieve a solution balance. The 6-8 ppm level is recommended providing we can get the calcium level to be five times the magnesium level (or about 30-40 ppm). This recommendation also hinges on the fact that we would like to have the potassium at two times the magnesium level (or 12-16 ppm). Keeping sodium in check below the 6-8 ppm level completes the ideal balance for these four nutrients. Unfortunately, it doesn't always come out that way, and we must work the balance backward when one or more of the nutrients are exceeding the strategic levels. Magnesium can compete quite effectively with potassium and must be kept in balance as much as possible.

An ideal soil nutrient balance:
Magnesium = 6-8 ppm
Calcium = 30-40 ppm
Potassium = 12-16 ppm
Sodium = 6-8 ppm

Liming sandy soils with a dolomitic lime is a good, cheap way to add magnesium providing that magnesium is in short supply. The quality of your lime is critical. I prefer a very fine lime (graded somewhere between pulverized and superfine). Very fine limes will pass 60-80% through a 100-mesh screen. I would prefer to make smaller but more frequent applications than trying to use a larger amount in one of two applications of a coarser lime and hoping the calcium and magnesium will become available when needed. When the soil pH is above the 6.5 level an alternative magnesium source should be used. If potassium is also low, K-Mag (also known as sul-po-mag) could be used to help solve both issues. K-Mag is approximately 20-22% potassium, 11% magnesium, and 20-22% sulfur. In situations where potassium is adequate, magnesium oxysulfate or magnesium sulfate could be used.

## Potassium

A good range for potassium is at 12-15 ppm, but this may not be high enough for grasses or alfalfa crops that cannot be intermittently fertilized. This recommended ppm level might even be too low at times for corn which takes up the bulk of its potassium between 7-leaf collar and tasseling maturity stages. For crops such as these it is important to push standard test levels of potassium to 7-10% base saturation to provide a good feed rate of potassium into solution for this period of rapid crop uptake. Luxury consumption of potassium does tend to be a problem in grasses and hays, so limiting the number of applications may exacerbate this problem in these crops. Pushing the potassium level up too high may create a magnesium deficiency due to potassium interference. Low exchange capacity soils would benefit from the addition of zeolite products, which contain low solubility potassium. Using zeolite products would be much the same as using low soluble rock phosphate as a partial phosphorus source. Highly soluble potassium sources such as potassium sulfate (0-0-50) or muriate of potash (0-0-60) could be used to elevate low levels. Care should be taken in the use of muriate of potash so as not to create a chloride issue. K-Mag is also a soluble source of potassium and is an ideal product especially if magnesium is needed in the system. One of the best sources of potassium is composted manure or natural waste products such as leaves or grass clippings. Although low in analysis and requiring a large amount of material, the benefit of adding organic matter in low exchange capacity soils is priceless.

## Sodium

Sodium at less than 8 ppm is generally not hard to achieve as long the other cations (Ca, Mg or K) are in line and irrigation is not taking place. Sodium contamination is most often the result of poor quality irrigation water, although I have seen sodium excesses as a result of spreading salt on adjacent roads and then having it leach off-site into the low area of a nearby growing field. Elevating the calcium, magnesium and potassium and flushing the site is the best way to handle high sodium levels.

If the sodium is 30 ppm and calcium, magnesium and potassium meet the desired threshold limits for a high sodium soil, I would work the soil balance backward to offset the high sodium levels. Therefore if the potassium should be twice as high as the sodium I would set the potassium level at 60 ppm. Now the magnesium needs to be elevated to 30 ppm. The calcium should be five times higher than the magnesium level, so the calcium needs to be moved up to 150 ppm. This will help maintain a soluble nutrient balance, but it will only work well until the point when you create a toxic soluble salt issue for your plants.

Flushing excess sodium out with irrigation water or rainwater is still the most sensible method to deal with high levels. If your irrigation water contains 20 ppm sodium, then irrigation techniques become critical and elevating the balance as shown earlier becomes necessary. The use of good soil surfactants may also help in the soil flushing process.

---

## Boron

Boron should fall between 0.05 and 0.10 ppm. This range is acceptable as long as the humidity is low. Boron, like calcium, travels one direction up into the plant via the xylem and depends upon evapotranspiration to move the nutrient upward. Plants such as wheat or turfgrasses that grow rapidly in early spring will have a better than average chance to be boron deficient due to the cool, wet growing conditions at this time of year.

A five-year tissue summary on wheat test results indicated that boron was deficient an average of 82% of the time when at the pre-joint stage. Due to the early spring weather conditions that wheat and turfgrass face, it is best to foliar feed plants boron. Boron can be added to the soil, but can be precipitated out as calcium borate in highly calcareous soils. When free in solution boron, like nitrogen, is also leachable.

---

## Iron

I have never seen an iron problem show up on a soil test. This is because most of the clay particles that are present in soils are made up of iron and aluminum. Certainly high soil pH levels, above 7, which contain excess bicarbonates, can reduce uptake of iron in the plant. Some herbicides such as glyphosate can also tie up the iron in a plant. It is difficult to look at a soil or paste analysis and feel comfortable about predicting an iron deficiency. I normally disregard the iron numbers on a paste analysis because if a few clay particles slip past the filter paper during the extraction process the ICP equipment will pick these up and show them as soluble iron or aluminum. I see the same phenomenon happening for tissue or feed analysis when soil contamination on the leaves at the time of sampling shows up as high iron and aluminum numbers in the plant analysis. Washing plant material before tissue analysis is imperative in order to get meaningful data.

## Manganese

Manganese should be greater than 0.07 ppm but less than 0.25 ppm. Be warned that values above the 0.25 ppm level could result in manganese toxicity in the plant. Note that values above the 0.07 ppm level will generally supply adequate amounts of manganese to plants unless glyphosate herbicides have been used the previous year or manganese is applied to genetically modified plants such as soybeans which are glyphosate tolerant. Glyphosate applications tend to chelate or bind manganese along with other trace metals for a period of time. Depending on the level of trace elements initially in the plant when glyphosate is applied, the plant may enter into a state of suspended animation if it goes into a deficiency mode. This may last for 8-10 days depending upon the recovery rate. If this does occur then the plant essentially has its growing season shortened by this recovery time. High soil pH, loose soils, or dry soils will also contribute to inducing deficiencies in the plant. Soybeans and many of the specialty crops have a high response to manganese so having manganese levels around 0.1 ppm would be an excellent goal. On soils not making the minimum levels, I would consider foliar feeding the plants rather than broadcasting manganese sulfate—especially if the soils are muck or high exchange capacity soils. My five-year tissue analysis study for corn, beans and wheat showed corn and beans were deficient in manganese at early stages in their development a little over half the time. Wheat was averaging deficient levels 27% of the time but this number increased up to almost 50% during dry seasons.

## Copper

Copper solubility levels should be between 0.05 to 0.08 ppm. Plants pick up copper primarily through direct root intercept (Figure 4). Under elevated levels of compaction the recommended 0.05-0.08 ppm levels for copper may not be sufficient. For that matter all the established solubility levels may not be sufficient to satisfy the plants' needs. Based on the five-year tissue study, copper uptake was a particular problem for beans and winter wheat. Copper deficiencies are enhanced by the fact that winter wheat is trying to develop a root system in the first part of its life cycle during cool and generally wet conditions. Most of the wheat, like soybeans, are no-tilled into a previous crop and expected to develop under more compacted soil conditions. The analysis of the results from the five-year tissue study showed that soybeans and wheat showed copper deficiencies early in their development (at 78% and 89% respectively).

---

## Zinc

Zinc solubility levels should range between 0.08 and 0.10 ppm. The vast majority of soils that I have worked with generally approach the minimum equipment testing detection limit of 0.02 ppm. This was quite a shock to me since over the past 30 years of consulting, I have recommended the application of tons of zinc sulfate to be soil applied. Soil applications of zinc may be somewhat questionable now. However soils with very low zinc levels will never improve if only foliar applications are used.

A combination of foliar and soil application makes the most sense. The grasses seem to be the most sensitive to low soluble zinc levels. The five-year tissue study showed corn and wheat to be deficient 87% and 88% of the time, respectively. Soybeans on the average were deficient 40% of the time, but had reached a deficiency level as high as 74% during wet years. I believe the most effective way to apply zinc is through a foliar application, but this is not as easy as it may sound. The grasses, especially corn, need zinc very early. This may be as early as the 2-leaf collar stage. Putting zinc in the row starter seems to be the most logical fix, but I have never been able to totally resolve a zinc deficiency in the plant according to tissue analysis. Some limited data has shown a yield response of nearly 2 bushels per acre even though we could not detect an increase in the tissue analysis at the 4-5 leaf collar stage. It is quite possible that the fields we tissue tested improved in size and/or yield potential, but threshold levels were never met.

One of the first nutrients to tie up zinc is phosphorus. Even chelated zinc, which is protected until the chelate bonding breaks apart, is still lying in a bed of reactive phosphorus when the breakdown occurs. Treatment using zinc on corn and wheat seeds has shown significant improvement in plant size and weight when compared with side by side samples at the 6-leaf collar stage.

Yield response after seed treating with zinc has been varied from 0-20 bushels per acre. The fields that showed the best response were those that had moderate levels of zinc in the soil.

Those fields with very low zinc levels did not show a yield response even though the weights and tissue values at the 6-leaf collar stage were better. For those soils low in zinc, both seed treatment and foliar feeding should be done in order to reach the threshold levels in the plants. Comparisons can easily be made using corn by splitting the planter seed boxes. However, testing the response of starter mixes with and without zinc is much more difficult without using GPS tracking equipment.

Another interesting relationship that seems to appear between zinc and phosphorus is the ability of zinc to enhance phosphorus uptake in corn. I was puzzled why over 50% of corn fields were deficient in phosphorus when the corn was tissue sampled before the 6-leaf collar stage. Nearly 95% of my clients had added starter fertilizer using their corn planters and placed the fertilizer 2 x 2 (2 inches to the side and 2 inches down) from the seed. The pre-6 leaf collar stage (Figure 24) did not offer a strong correlation to zinc and phosphorus either, but the ear leaf tissue samples (Figure 25) showed a nice correlation between the two nutrients.

# Phosphorus and Zinc Deficiency Levels in Corn (Pre-6 Leaf Collar Stage)

| Year | Phosphorus Deficiency Percentage | Zinc Deficiency Percentage |
|---|---|---|
| 2002 | 43 | 76 |
| 2003 | 28 | 87 |
| 2004 | 54 | 88 |
| 2005 | 59 | 86 |
| 2006 | 72 | 96 |
| 2007 & 2008 | 72 | 97 |

**Fig. 24** *Phosphorus and zinc deficiency levels at the corn pre-6 leaf collar stage did not show a big correlation between these two nutrient levels.*

# Phosphorus and Zinc Deficiency Levels in Corn (Ear Leaf Stage)

| Year | Phosphorus Deficiency Percentage | Zinc Deficiency Percentage |
|---|---|---|
| 2002 | n/a | n/a |
| 2003 | n/a | n/a |
| 2004 | 56 | 67 |
| 2005 | 29 | 36 |
| 2006 | 100 | 100 |
| 2007 & 2008 | 67 | 93 |

**Fig. 25** *Phosphorus and zinc deficiency levels at the corn ear leaf stage did show a relationship between the two nutrients.*

I believe that the starter fertilizer used did have enough impact on the 6-leaf collar stage data to prevent a visual correlation between phosphorus and zinc. It wasn't until the ear leaf stage that the starter fertilizer effect was minimized and that relationship then became apparent. After seeing this relationship between zinc and phosphorus, the following year I set up three plots and sprayed zinc, manganese and a combination of zinc and manganese foliar on the plants at the 2, 3, 4 and 5-leaf collar stage. I cut plants at the 6-leaf collar stage, weighed and analyzed them for nutrients. Those plants sprayed with zinc had better phosphorus levels and plant weights—especially when sprayed at the 2-leaf collar growth stage. Another interesting fact was that corn seeds treated with zinc still responded the best at the 2-leaf collar stage and the next best time to spray zinc was at the 5-leaf collar stage. I believe the best way to correct a zinc deficiency is through seed treatment and a foliar application where 1/4 to 1/2 pound of actual zinc metal is applied before the 5-leaf collar stage. I prefer to use the flowable zinc products which have some time-release attributes to them.

As this book goes into print we will have one year behind us where a trace mineral pack with as much as 1.1 lbs. of acutal zinc supplied in a starter fertilizer mix has been used. The preliminary indication looks very positive with very good yields and increased girth on the corn ears. Many clients have already expressed an interest in using the product next year. There will be some adjustment to the product based on tissue data collected in the initial trial.

# Chapter 4

# Balancing Nutrients on High Exchange Capacity Soils

---

THE BEST APPROACH TO BALANCING SOILS WITH EXCHANGE CAPACITIES over 10 is with the basic cation saturation ratio (BCSR) approach. The BCSR in combination with the paste test and tissue analysis really improves field results. Plants tend to grow to the level of the least available nutrient, therefore anything that restricts root mass such as compaction, insect feeding, or mechanical root pruning greatly limits the effect of balancing soils.

---

## Guidelines for High TEC Soils

The starting nutrient guideline for a standard soil report using the Mehlich III extraction solution (at 1 part soil to 10 parts extracting solution) is outlined in Figure 32. There is a very large range in the guidelines for the cations. This results from balancing the cations over a wide range of exchange capacities. The total exchange capacity of the soil is measured in milliequivalents and results from the summation of cations measured in the extracting solution. Many labs report the pounds of nutrients found in the soil, but how do you calculate exactly how many pounds of each cation should be in your soil based on the Albrecht recommended values of 65% calcium, 15% magnesium and 5% potassium? Logan Labs, which I use, will do this calculation when requested, but for those who don't have access to this service the calculation is relatively simple if you know the following relationships between one milliequivalent and lbs. of nutrient per acre.

---

Total Exchange Capacity Nutrient Relationships

1.0 mEq of hydrogen = 20 lbs. of hydrogen in an acre furrow slice

1.0 mEq of calcium = 400 lbs. of calcium in an acre furrow slice

1.0 mEq of magnesium = 240 lbs. of magnesium in an acre furrow slice

1.0 mEq of potassium = 780 lbs. of potassium in an acre furrow slice

1.0 mEq of sodium = 460 lbs. of sodium in an acre furrow slice

---

Now let's calculate the required levels of calcium, magnesium and potassium that are needed to balance a 20 TEC soil using the BCSR method. According to the guidelines in Figure 32, the calcium base saturation level should be 65%, the magnesium level should be 12% and the potassium level should be 5%. We should always try to maintain at least 10% of the base saturation with hydrogen. This means that in this situation we have accounted for 92% of the cations based on our desired levels. The other 7% could be divided between the above listed cations with some consideration to the crop being raised and its growth requirements. For example, most specialty crops need a high level of potassium, so instead of 5% potassium you might want to push that up to the 7 or 8% level.

---

Using our example, a 20 TEC soil should have the following:

(TEC x recommended % nutrient = mEq value of nutrient)

20 mEq x 0.65 (percent of calcium) = 13.0 mEq of calcium
20 mEq x 0.15 (percent of magnesium) = 3.0 mEq of magnesium
20 mEq x 0.05 (percent of potassium) = 1.0 mEq of potassium

Desired cation levels:

(mEq of nutrient x nutrient equivalent from previous box = lbs. of nutrient)

---

13.0 mEq of calcium x 400 lbs. of calcium per 1.0 mEq =
5,200 lbs. of calcium
3.0 mEq of magnesium x 240 lbs. of magnesium per 1.0 mEq =
720 lbs. of magnesium
1.0 mEq of potassium x 780 lbs. of potassium per 1.0 mEq =
780 lbs. of potassium

The above calculations could be done on every soil sample and the deficit or excess could be determined. Deficits are the easiest to handle when it comes to balancing soils. Simply choose a product that contains one or more of the deficient nutrients and add it to the soil. This process will be discussed in much more detail during the review of each nutrient later in this chapter. Getting rid of excess cations is a lot more difficult and will also be discussed in detail later.

## pH

On heavier soils, I would like to see the soil pH level very close to 6.2 (plus or minus 0.2). This pH level will allow for the maximum solubility of soil nutrients. Liming low pH soils should be done in phases and not just dumped on heavily with one application. I would apply up to a maximum of 2 tons of lime per acre (providing incorporation could be done). On very rare occasions I have applied more, such as in situations with muck soils having a very high exchange capacity and a very low pH. Liming will be discussed in detail in the calcium section. Lowering the pH with elemental sulfur will be covered in the sulfur section.

## Organic Matter

A soil with organic matter (OM) levels greater than 4% would be ideal. I work with very few farms that are consistently at the 4% or greater organic matter level. Although heavier soils normally have plenty of nutrient-holding capacity, it's the organic matter that dramatically affects the workability and drainage of the heavier soils.

Organic matter in conjunction with good calcium to magnesium ratios is essential for maintaining a good air to water ratio in the soil profile. Many times I hear people talk about increasing organic matter as if it was an easy thing to do. I personally question whether organic matter can be increased on a normal corn, bean and wheat rotation even if the tillage changes from conventional plowing to conservation tillage or no-till. Changing your tillage from conventional to no-till can certainly increase the surface organic matter, but when averaged in over the normal depth of plowing it will not be an overall increase. When no-till started gaining real popularity in the 1980s I heard people claim they had doubled their organic matter after a few short years. It was not until the mid-1990s that the laboratories doing soil testing stopped using volumetric means of organic matter testing and switched to a weight-based analysis. Only the weight-based analysis will give you the best indication of trend lines.

> 1 acre furrow slice (AFS) of soil =
> 1 square acre x 6 inches deep = 2,000,000 lbs.

Doing the math seems the best way to consider the feasibility of raising organic matter. Assuming you have soil with 2% organic matter and you want to double it, how much residue would it take to decompose and raise the organic matter another 2 percent? There are many variables in this complicated process so we need to make a few assumptions. First, an acre furrow slice (AFS) of soil is one square acre and 6 inches deep. The acre furrow slice weighs approximately 2 million lbs. There are reports that say 100 lbs. of organic residue completely reduced to humus will yield 1 pound of humus under ideal conditions. With these two assumptions we can do the math. A 2% organic matter soil has 40,000 lbs. of humus in the soil (2,000,000 x 2%). Therefore to double the organic matter level in the soil, we will need to add 40,000 lbs. of humus. If 100 lbs. of residue decomposes to one pound (100:1 ratio) of humus, then we will need 4,000,000 lbs. (40,000 lbs. humus x 100) of residue per acre to decompose into humus.

I have seen estimates that a good corn crop with stalks and roots could yield 15,000-20,000 lbs. of residue. At the high end it would take 200 corn crops and a lot more wheat and bean crops to double the humus levels in the soil by just 2%—assuming no oxidation of the existing humus or loss due to erosion occurred. Even if the numbers are off by 50%, we would not be able to double the humus levels in a person's lifetime. The real take-home message in this is protect your current organic matter levels as much as humanly possible. Humus is the lifeblood of the soil and worth more than gold.

## Sulfur

The sulfur level in heavy soils would be ideal if it was around 30 ppm. It could be higher when growing corn or another high nitrogen crop, but exceeding a 5:1 ratio of nitrogen to sulfur in the soil would not be economical. Sulfur levels can be used as an indicator of poor drainage. If the sulfur in the soils is abnormally high compared to the application rates that you applied of sulfur, watch for possible drainage issues arising in the soil. Subsoiling with a deep till tool could help improve the situation. If subsoiling is not an option because of shallow tile or rocks, a soil-wetting agent may help. Elemental sulfur can also be used to lower pH levels. I use the following table (Figure 26) as a guideline for application amounts.

*(Elemental)*

# Application Rates for Sulfur
## for Desired pH Change

| Desired change in pH level | Sulfur (lbs./acre) | | |
|---|---|---|---|
| | Sands | Loams | Clays |
| 8.5 - 6.5 | 2,000 | 2,500 | 3,000 |
| 8.0 - 6.5 | 1,200 | 1,500 | 2,000 |
| 7.5 - 6.5 | 500 | 800 | 1,000 |
| 7.0 - 6.5 | 100 | 150 | 300 |

**Fig. 26** *Sulfur rates needed to change pH for sand, loam and clay based soils.*

If the basic makeup of the soil were of calcium, such as found in calcareous sand or clay with snail shells, I would not attempt to try and lower the pH. The reservoir of calcium is entirely too vast to be able to economically make much of a pH change. Much of the breakdown of the elemental sulfur will be done biologically in the soil and therefore good incorporation and patience are needed to get a reduction in pH.

Other good sources of sulfur include ammonium sulfate (21-0-0) which is one of the more acidic nitrogen sources, potassium sulfate, or K-Mag (know previously as sul-po-mag or to the feed industry as dynamite). The sulfur content of the more common sources is listed in the following table.

## Sources of Sulfur

| Sulfur Source | Percent Sulfur |
|---|---|
| Elemental Sulfur | 95 |
| Ammonium Sulfate (21-0-0) | 24 |
| Potassium Sulfate (0-0-50) | 18 |
| Potassium Magnesium Sulfate (Sul-Po-Mag) | 22 |
| Gypsum | 12 |

**Fig. 27** *Various sulfur sources and the percentage of sulfur available for each type.*

Manures and biosolids (sludge) also carry various amounts of sulfur within them. When buying manures or biosolids, the value of sulfur is only notable up to the level that the crop requires. For example, a manure at a 3 ton per acre application supplies 90 lbs. of sulfur per acre, but since the corn crop only needs 40 lbs., the remaining 50 lbs. of sulfur should not be figured into the sulfur value of the manure. Also note that the sulfate form of sulfur (like nitrate) is leachable and may not be around for the next crop.

## Phosphorus

Phosphorus levels on the standard soil report should be 250 lbs. per acre as $P_2O_5$. Higher values are not a worry except for the ensuing environmental impact. Most of the phosphorus levels in streams and lakes are from the loss of soil from fields containing various levels of phosphorus. No-till or minimum tillage fields might have levels as low as 150 lbs. per acre and still be a threat to water contamination because of phosphorus stratification in the soil. I ran into a stratification problem for a client of mine a few years ago who had been no-tilling and minimum tilling for over 25 years.

Figure 28 shows a report and study that I did concerning the phosphorus stratification issue. I ran a wheat tissue analysis for a client of mine who felt the color just wasn't quite right on his crop. The tissue analysis (done on April 21) indicated a number of problems, but the biggest of these, which contributed to the off-color symptom, were phosphorus and probable nitrogen deficiencies (Figure 28). The first sampling apparently had picked up some residual nitrogen in the analysis from a 28% nitrogen topdress application. When the wheat field was resampled in the first week of May the situation was getting worse. The weather was extremely dry for this time of year, and by the time the second sampling was complete the wheat was starting into a number of deficiencies. Visually the color of the wheat was not too bad at the time.

In grass crops I typically see phosphorus, sulfur and zinc go deficient at the same time nitrogen becomes limiting. In this wheat example phosphorus and zinc were already deficient, but sulfur declined substantially from the previous tissue test. By the time we hit the flag leaf stage some rain had occurred and the flag leaf tissue data had substantially improved—with the exception of potassium and zinc.

Although the wheat recovery was very impressive and could have been more complete with a foliar application at the pre-joint stage, damage to the kernel count would have already been done prior to the jointing stage. Nutrient levels are critical during kernel development as well as during the filling period. In this case, improving the kernel numbers during the development period with better phosphorus and zinc levels would mean very little if potassium goes deficient and impedes the kernel filling process. The result is aborted or light, chaffy kernels.

The soil analysis indicated that there was over 250 lbs. of easily extractable phosphorus. So how could a soil with an optimum level end up with a tissue deficiency? *Lesson one is never to trust a soil analysis by itself.* Tissue analysis is really the only way to verify plant health and the level of nutrient uptake.

Phosphorus uptake in the roots occurs primarily through the process of diffusion. Therefore good root development is essential for adequate phosphorus uptake in the plant. Microbial activity is also important in solubilizing phosphorus, with temperature and aeration being equally important.

## Wheat Tissue Analyses

| | N % | P % | K % | S % | Ca % | Mg % | B ppm | Fe ppm | Cu ppm | Mn ppm | Zn ppm |
|---|---|---|---|---|---|---|---|---|---|---|---|
| Desired Tissue Level | 4.2 | 0.46 | 4.4 | 0.30 | 0.47 | 0.16 | 7.0 | 50 | 10.8 | 45.0 | 52.0 |
| 90% Level | 3.80 | 0.41 | 4.00 | 0.27 | 0.42 | 0.14 | 6.3 | 45.0 | 9.7 | 41.0 | 46.8 |
| BF Tent | 5.10 | 0.38 | 3.19 | 0.39 | 0.38 | 0.14 | 4.1 | 326 | 3.9 | 94.0 | 21.0 |
| BF Tent 5/04 | 2.82 | 0.32 | 3.14 | 0.21 | 0.26 | 0.13 | 1.9 | 259 | 3.7 | 44.6 | 29.8 |
| BF Tent Flag | 3.56 | 0.30 | 1.91 | 0.42 | 0.76 | 0.19 | 4.60 | 126 | 5.9 | 52.7 | 21.4 |
| Flag Leaf Desired | 3.2 | 0.30 | 3.30 | 0.25 | 0.50 | 0.12 | 10.0 | 50 | 8.0 | 40.0 | 32 |

**Fig. 28** *A comparison at various wheat stages and the desired levels of nutrients under tissue analysis.*

In this wheat situation two problems were occurring at the same time—as is often the case in nature. Initially I perceived the problem to be one of phosphorus stratification, however in the process of checking for stratification I also found a compaction issue. This farm has not seen a plow for over 25 years. The current tillage method is no-till and or a combination of the AerWay method and no-till. The wheat prior to planting was AerWay tilled, but over the course of the winter and spring, the silty clay loam soils ran back together and became very hard —especially when dry conditions set in. The compaction by itself was enough to induce phosphorus deficiency in the wheat.

I was curious to find out if there was a stratification problem and if so, by how much. After discussing the situation with Susan Shaner of Logan Labs, she agreed to fund a research study done at two locations on this field with soil sampled at a 1.5-inch incremental depth. The field was located in Seneca County in Ohio on the farm of Bob Featheringill. Bob is an excellent farmer who has won numerous awards for his efforts in soil and water conservation. The study consisted of sampling the north and south ends of the field. Several cores where taken across the areas and the respective depths were put into appropriate bags giving a composite sample for each 1.5 inch increment. The sites were sampled to 7.5 inches. A full depth sample was collected at each sampling site and combined to form a composite sample on each of the north and south ends.

## Stratification Study Soil Core Sample

**Fig. 29** *A picture of a core sample collected for the wheat field stratification study. The total depth was 7.5 inches with a composite sample collected from both the north and south ends of the field.*

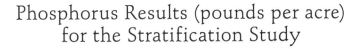
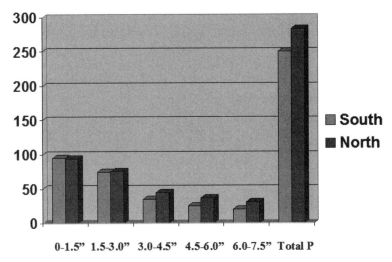

**Fig. 30** *Phosphorus amounts shown in pounds per acre for the north and south ends (and totals) of the stratification study field.*

Part of the data collected in the soil stratification study is represented in Figure 30. Overall, phosphorus showed the most dramatic decline in the soil levels with respect to depth. Approximately 68% of the phosphorus in the south section and 60% in the north section was located in the top 3 inches of the soil. Consider the ramifications of planting row crop seeds 1-2 inches deep—as much as 40% of your phosphorus could be above the seed and relatively unavailable.

Compaction and dry weather could easily seal the fate of any phosphorus availability. Row crop clients who have been no-till farming for quite some time and using no starter fertilizer could seriously jeopardize plant health—especially under stress conditions. Assuming surface phosphorus may be unavailable due to seeding depths, phosphorus at the deeper depths may also be unavailable due to the cool soil temperatures. As planting dates get pushed up earlier and earlier this issue will be exacerbated.

Turfgrass clients might escape the seeding depth issue but dry weather and compaction, along with poor water quality for irrigation, can be just as devastating to the phosphorus availability. Whether you are growing row crops or turfgrass, applying lime, gypsum and trace elements such as iron, manganese and zinc will rapidly reduce the solubility of phosphorus.

Since phosphorus will barely move more than a half inch into the soil following a surface application, the high exchange capacity soils—which generally have a lower infiltration rates—are at risk to soil and nutrient loss from high rainfall events. It is my opinion that these soils should be moldboard plowed every 5 to 7 years. I know this will really upset the staunch no-tillers, but water contamination is a real issue and some university data has indicated that conservation tillage has not fixed the problem of high phosphorus levels in the surface water. I suggest plowing once every six years following a wheat crop and then working the soil down and planting a cover crop. The cover crop would help prevent soil erosion and the plowing would help incorporate the nutrients accumulated at the surface to a deeper depth. This would aid the crops during the following year with nutrient uptake, especially during dry periods when the available moisture and root activity is deeper in the soil.

---

## Your Soil Report
## and Understanding Soil Stratification Issues

Have you ever gotten a soil test back and it looked pretty good but the area that it came from was not performing well? The lab must have made a mistake, right? Wrong. It has been my experience that the laboratory is generally correct. Although not infallible, the lab with its quality control measures normally catches most of its errors. I would guess that nine out of 10 times the rechecks that I have asked for have come back the same. So what might explain the difference between the analysis and the field results? The first thing that I would consider is stratification, especially for those samples collected in turf or long-term no-till.

As a consultant I have to continually remind myself of the stratification issue. When we take a soil sample and send it to the lab, it is easy to think of the sample as a homogeneous mixture regardless of what depth the sample was collected. Nutrients applied to the soil do not easily move through the profile unless aided by some sort of tillage. Nutrients interact with each other enhancing or lowering the solubility of each other.

Phosphorus is one of the most difficult nutrients to move through the soil, even in sands. Phosphorus reacts with almost all the cations reducing its availability and staying within a fraction of an inch of where it was applied.

Calcium is the cation that is most often applied as a calcitic or dolomitic lime. The solubility of lime is approximately 5% at a pH of 7. This does not change because of fineness or type of lime.

Therefore lime applied to turf or in a no-till situation lies on the surface and dissolves raising the pH in the shallow zone to 7 or above. This reduces the solubility of the lime to 5% which slows the movement of calcium into the profile. The other problem inherent with stratified calcium is the effect that it has on root development. Calcium primarily travels through the xylem, or the water transport system, and is one directional. Unlike phosphorus or potassium, which can be picked up by surface roots and transported to roots lower in the soil, calcium must be at the root tips to sustain a healthy root system.

How do we overcome the stratification issue? First we must be aware that it exists and possibly change up our sampling technique to monitor the different depths to see the extent this issue may exist. For those in a no-till situation it may be as simple as doing some tillage—as painful as that may sound. In turf, collecting cores during aeration and top dressing with a pretested and appropriately balanced soil mix will go a long way to addressing this problem. The use of gypsum, which is not influenced by pH for solubility, is better than lime for surface applications. Remember that any calcium source will precipitate out soluble phosphorus.

Stratification issues are exacerbated by soil compaction. On those soils prone to compaction desired levels may need to be increased. Although this is treating the symptom and not the problem, it may be a temporary solution.

*The Soil Probe Newsletter, Logan Labs*

Raising and maintaining phosphorus levels can be accomplished with a wide variety of products. The main commercial products such as monoammonium phosphate (MAP) and diammonium phosphate (DAP) are the most soluble and readily available products. The two products are very similar with the exception of the number of ammonium ions attached to the phosphate ion. DAP has two ammonium ions whereas MAP has only one ammonium ion. The initial soil reaction from DAP is approximately at a pH level of 9 where MAP has an initial soil reaction of pH 4. DAP will eventually create more acidity as the two ammonium ions are converted to nitrate. I prefer to use MAP on the higher pH soils and DAP on the lower pH soils. These products are highly soluble and reactive to other cations in solution. At pH levels below 5, it is more likely that the phosphorus will be tied up by aluminum and iron. At the higher pH levels calcium and magnesium will precipitate out of the phosphorus in a form of rock phosphate.

High applications of soluble phosphorus can also create a zinc deficiency in the soil. My five-year tissue study consistently showed deficiencies of zinc—especially in the cereal crops. On the flip side, one of my field studies also indicated that plants deficient in zinc did not pick up phosphorus as well (Figures 24 and 25).

Manures and biosolids—if you are located in proximity to a source of these waste products—are viable phosphorus sources, as well as nitrogen and potassium. Depending on the manure or biosolid type, calcium may also be in the nutrient profile at varying amounts.

Rock phosphate has also been used as a phosphorus source. This product has been quite controversial as to its real benefit. The solubility of rock phosphate is low according to its true nature, but that doesn't necessarily mean that it is completely bad. It is certainly not a product that will supply readily useable phosphorus the day it is applied, but it can be used to supply a buildup of phosphorus. Due to the low solubility of rock phosphate it is much better to have a very fine grind of the product (100- to 200-mesh). Grind any material fine enough, along with thorough incorporation, and you can get solubility. The fine grind of the rock phosphate will make it a lot harder to handle and spread.

I recently had Logan Labs check the solubility of a coarse rock phosphate sample from Tennessee. The solubility was checked at four different pH levels, 7.5, 7.0, 6.5 and 6.0. The following is the ICP test data (in ppm) of the various solutions using 1.0 gram of rock phosphate in 100 ml of the pH-adjusted distilled water. Hydrochloric acid was used to lower the pH.

It was my intention to apply the rock phosphate on only soils with a pH below 7. At these lower pH levels it appears that the rock phosphate is a better source of aluminum, calcium, iron and potassium than phosphorus. Calculating out at 1,000 lb. per application would yield about 82 grams or 0.2 lbs. of phosphorus per acre. The results show that there was as much iron, 1.75 times aluminum and five times as much calcium released as phosphorus, all of which can precipitate out phosphorus. It was not until a pH level of 4.5 that any significant amount of phosphorus became soluble. Significant amounts of aluminum and calcium were also soluble at this low pH level. Using this coarse rock phosphate could easily be picked up in a soil test using Mehlich III extracting solution with a pH of 2.5, but plant availability could be a whole different ballgame. Based on this data I don't see how this product will be a great substitute for commercial phosphorus sources. Granted, reactions in the soil could be different, especially over time.

# Rock Phosphate Solubility

| | pH | | | | |
|---|---|---|---|---|---|
| | **7.5** | **7** | **6.5** | **6** | **4.5** |
| Al | 233.6 | 237.4 | 288.2 | 317.8 | 1,661 |
| B | 5.074 | 5.447 | 5.3 | 5.21 | 12.3 |
| Ca | 671.9 | 715.3 | 830.8 | 1,069 | 3,632 |
| Cu | 0.313 | 0.3 | 0.32 | 0.271 | 2.378 |
| Fe | 136.2 | 141.6 | 166.8 | 186 | 997.8 |
| K | 118 | 100.9 | 183.6 | 221.8 | 578.8 |
| Mg | 60.05 | 44.9 | 62.95 | 101.7 | 181.3 |
| Mn | 11.67 | 13.46 | 15.8 | 17.04 | 87.8 |
| P | 151 | 143 | 168 | 181 | 1,200 |
| S | 40.76 | 54.37 | 78.8 | 105.4 | 115 |
| Zn | 0.788 | 0.466 | 0.52 | 0.627 | 3.9 |

**Fig. 31** *Rock phosphate solubility is tested at four pH levels (6.0, 6.5, 7.0 and 7.5) from a Tennessee sample. Phosphorus solubility was consistent at pH levels from 6.0 through 7.5 and only showed significant increase at a pH level of 4.5.*

# Desired Nutrient Levels
# for High Exchange Capacity Soils TE

|  | Desired Levels |
|---|---|
| Soil pH | 6.2-6.3 |
| Organic matter % | >4.0 |
| Sulfur ppm | 30-40 |
| Mehlich III Phosphorus lbs./ac. | 250 |
|  |  |
| Calcium lbs./ac. | 2,600-7,800 |
| Magnesium lbs./ac. | 360-1,080 |
| Potassium lbs./ac. | 400-1,200 |
| Sodium lbs./ac. | 40-80 |
| Base Saturation % |  |
| Calcium % | 65-68 |
| Magnesium % | 12-15 |
| Potassium % | 5-7 |
| Sodium % | 0.5-1.0 |
| Exchangeable Hydrogen % | 10 |
|  |  |
| Boron ppm | 0.7-1.0 |
| Iron ppm | >50 |
| Manganese ppm | 40-60 |
| Copper ppm | 3.5-5.5 |
| Zinc ppm | 8-10 |
| Aluminum ppm | <1,000 |

**Fig. 32** *The range of desired levels of nutrients in high TEC soils, greater than 11, measured in lbs. per acre.*

## Calcium

The cations on the high TEC soils should be balanced using the basic cation saturation ratios (BCSR) that Bear, Toth and Albrecht developed in the mid 1940s. It is important to point out that these gentlemen did not develop the method of soil testing, just the ratio balance. Figure 32 shows the desired base saturation levels for the four main cations: calcium, magnesium, potassium and sodium. The lb. per acre values appear to have a very wide range, but these numbers are based on exchange capacities in soils ranging from 11 to 26. I prefer to use the BCSR method for balancing heavier soils since these soils have enough clay content to develop structure. Good structure in heavier soils is critical for root development therefore I want the best chemistry balance which will lead to maximum soil structure. Many people criticize this approach, but I have personally seen the benefit in the field (along with my clients). This balance is not something that you can achieve in one year; it takes many years with constant monitoring to attain. This is like the process of dieting to get to your ideal weight which depends on where you start and how dedicated you are to the process. It doesn't happen overnight.

I was very fortunate early in my consulting career to be confronted by a client concerning this idea of balance. I was in my first year of consulting when I delivered a set of reports to a father and son farming team. The field that we were discussing was a problem field that had a pH of 7.3 and about a 50% calcium and 35% magnesium base saturation. I indicated that we would like to adjust the base saturation balance to about 65% calcium and 15% magnesium. This was the philosophy that the Brookside Laboratories consulting group, of which I belonged, upheld.

The method by which one gets to this destination may be different for each person, but the end result that I wanted was 65% calcium and 15% magnesium. Adding to the soil calcium deficit was the easy part, but getting rid of an extra 20% of magnesium was going to be the tough part. I chose to flood the soil with 3 tons of high calcium lime and through mass action I would replace the magnesium with calcium and move it lower into the soil profile with the help of percolating water and subsoiling to break up a plowpan.

Upon hearing my recommendation of using 3 tons of high calcium lime, which was 50 miles away compared to dolomite lime which was 1 mile away (and the fact that I wanted to lime a soil which already had a high pH), the father pushed his chair back and said that this recommendation was a bunch of bunk (but not quite in those terms). I was immediately unnerved by the father's reaction and the fact that he left the room and did not return. The son though said not to worry for this was a problem field and he would do whatever it takes to bring it around. Two years later we put some gypsum on the field and followed a year later with two more tons of high calcium lime. On the 5th or 6th year of working to balance the field, I saw the father harvesting wheat and stopped to see how things were going. The father got out of the combine and asked me to take a look. He raked his heel in the soil and said, "Five years ago it would have taken an axe to get into this ground." Here was a man who thought that the balance idea was a bunch of bunk and knew nothing of soil chemistry, but after five years was thoroughly impressed with the results. From that day on I knew there was something to achieving balanced soils. This program would not have been nearly as successful had they not subsoiled and incorporated the lime. It took a combination of tillage and soil chemistry to make it all come together.

Calcium sources for soil applications primarily consist of three choices: dolomite lime, high-calcium lime or gypsum. There are also some blended sources such as lime stabilized biosolids or layer chicken manure that can contribute a significant amount of calcium in the application. When liming a soil consider the balance and pH first. Remember that the pH will affect the overall solubility of all the nutrients. If the pH is high due to excessive cations, there may be short-term consequences for liming a soil like it did in the father and son example previously shown.

In the 1970s we didn't pay any attention to solubility. Fertilizer was cheap and we slugged it on. It was not uncommon to find steel mill ammonium sulfate for $65-70 per ton and apply 500-600 lbs. per acre. This did two things: one was to supply a highly acidic nitrogen source to offset the lime and secondly it supplied a large amount of sulfate anions, which were necessary to help move magnesium out of the plow layer. The other advantage that we had back then was that there was still a lot of heavy tillage being done. Changing soil balance today will be a lot slower due to the reduced tillage used. As a result of our present reduced tillage methods liming needs to be done with smaller quantities such as 1,500-2,000 lbs. per acre, but applied more often. The solubility of lime drops to about 5-10% as the pH approaches 7. Therefore in the minimum tillage situations the surface pH can rapidly increase to 7 (or above) from a lime application and drop the solubility of lime to 10% or less. This not only ties up money, but also other nutrients—especially phosphorus.

As liming rates are reduced the fineness of our lime source needs to increase. We want reactivity, which means purchasing a lime with more than 60% passing through a 100-mesh screen. In the past liming has been something we might do every four or five years. For far too long lime and calcium have been treated as something different from the normal NPK nutrients. Soil testing should be done no less than every two or three years in order to keep the balance and pH into the desired narrow ranges (See Figure 32).

## Magnesium

Magnesium base saturation in heavier soils should be kept around 15%. Soils that are extremely high in clay content might even be better with magnesium saturation levels closer to 12%. The level of magnesium in the base saturation will directly impact soil physics or structure. This impact will include nutrient uptake, weed control, and water infiltration and percolation. It is easy to supply magnesium when the soil is deficient in this nutrient and also has a low pH. Dolomite lime is the most cost effective way to supply magnesium in these situations. If the pH is high due to excess calcium or sodium, I prefer to use K-Mag, magnesium oxysulfate, or magnesium sulfate if reasonably priced. The solubility of the limes drops to below 10% at high pH levels.

In minimum tillage or no-till situations, smaller, repeated applications are necessary. Soils with a very low pH level might need 4 to 6 tons of lime per acre. Assuming magnesium is needed, start out using 2 ton of dolomite lime per acre, then re-test a year or so later and let a soil test determine what kind of lime and the amount to use the next time. When building soil levels of magnesium, a product such as K-Mag in amounts in excess of 125-150 lbs. per acre will be needed for general crops in order to exceed crop removal.

## Potassium

The level of potassium should be balanced between 5 and 7% only. I would like to see 7% at the lower exchange capacities and dropping that to 5% at the highest exchange capacities. Potassium is a nutrient that I have struggled to get enough into the plant. Compaction and competing cations can easily reduce the uptake of potassium into the plant. It is imperative to maintain adequate levels of potassium in the plants since it affects water efficiency, disease resistance, and carbohydrate mobilization.

Grass and alfalfa hays tend to consume excessive potassium, presenting problems for balancing feed rations but also rapidly lowering soil potassium levels. Grains tend to remove minimal amounts of potassium, but the plants themselves require high levels of potassium in order to produce the grain (Figure 11).

Potassium chloride and potassium sulfate are the two most commercially available forms of potassium. I prefer to use potassium chloride for general agricultural crops, simply based on price. Organic farmers are forced to use potassium sulfate or manure as their potassium source.

Soils can tie up large amounts of potassium depending on the type of clay in the soil. When trying to buildup potassium keep in mind that the commercial sources are very soluble and can interfere with the uptake of magnesium. Therefore when I am trying to build potassium levels I think it's a good idea to use some K-Mag in an attempt to offset a possible magnesium interference issue. This may not be necessary if you have more than 18% magnesium in the base saturation. After applying potassium chloride (muriate of potash) the dissolved potassium in the soil solution can act as an extractant and move other cations into solution.

I saw this extracting effect of potassium when I had Logan Labs do a saturated paste test to see the potential potassium adsorptive capacity of a client's soil sample. The test was done as a saturated paste with a split sample. One of the soils was saturated with distilled water and one with 200 ppm potassium dissolved in distilled water. The leachates were vacuumed off after 24 hours and analyzed by the ICP.

The potassium absorbed by the soil was approximately 150 ppm or the equivalent to 900 lbs. per acre of 0-0-60 (muriate of potash). On the standard test the potassium was 445 lbs. per acre with a base saturation of 3.18 percent. Calcium and magnesium increased substantially in the soil solution with potassium chloride.

## Potassium Adsorptive Capacity in Soils

| K Level in Solution | Ca | Mg | K | Na | S | P | B | Mn | Fe | Cu | Zn |
|---|---|---|---|---|---|---|---|---|---|---|---|
| 0 | 6.9 | 2.2 | 4.4 | 1.5 | 0.84 | 0.00 | 0.05 | 0.07 | 6.06 | 0.01 | 0.02 |
| 200 ppm | 44.4 | 10.1 | 54.1 | 2.4 | 0.65 | 0.65 | 0.06 | 0.02 | 1.00 | 0.01 | 0.00 |
| +/− | +37.5 | +7.9 | -149.7 | +0.9 | -0.19 | +0.65 | +0.01 | -0.05 | -5.06 | 0.0 | -0.02 |

**Fig. 33** *The effect of a potassium solution on soil nutrient level.*

## Sodium

I would like to keep sodium in the 40-50 lbs. per acre level. High levels of sodium wreak havoc very quickly with the soil structure. Sodium has a very large hydrated radius, which keeps the clays from flocculating therefore destroying structure. A soil without good structure will be compacted with limited aeration and water-holding capacity. Sodium is so soluble that even soils within the 40-50 lb. per acre range on the standard test can have high levels of sodium in the paste test. This situation is especially true when the calcium solubility is low. This will be demonstrated later in the paste section of this book using the heavier soils.

## Hydrogen

The hydrogen ion concentration is directly related to the pH of the soil. It is important to maintain 10-12% base saturation of hydrogen ions in order to maximize solubility of the other nutrients. Oftentimes I hear people say that they don't have any hydrogen ions in the soil once the soil pH goes above 7. This is not quite an accurate statement. In order to have no hydrogen ions in the soil, the pH would have to be 14. At pH levels above 7, hydrogen ions are present—it is the exchangeable hydrogen ions that do not exist.

## Trace Elements

Soil trace element levels using the standard test are good starting points, but by no means are they the last word on availability. This fact is also true for all the major elements. For example, if the desired value of zinc is 8-10 ppm and the soil test comes back with 9 ppm, it does not mean that we can forget about zinc as a potential nutrient problem. Weather, soil physical conditions, pH, and the level of other nutrients in the soil do affect the availability of zinc—like all other nutrients. Some people feel that analyzing for trace elements in the soil is a waste of time. That is certainly possible if you don't look at paste analysis and tissue analysis. Ignorance is not bliss when dealing with soil test results. Trace elements are critical for top crop production and just because the standard test often does not correlate well with tissue tests does not mean we should ignore them. Tissue analysis often indicates that elevating trace element levels in the soil through broadcast applications is not very effective, but broadcasting traces in conjunction with foliar feeding trace elements may be our best way to supply deficient trace nutrients. The trace element guidelines that follow are based on the assumption that the soil pH is between 6 and 7, ideally at a 6.2 level.

## Boron

The standard soil report guideline for boron should range between 0.7 and 1.0 ppm. Boron, like nitrate, is taken up as an anion and primarily travels through the xylem or water transport system. Therefore any growing conditions which reduce evapotranspiration from the leaf may temporarily create a deficiency. I feel the most comfortable about adding boron to the soil than any other trace element, mainly because it is an anion.

Mixing a 10% granular form of borate with my phosphate or potash applications has been my method of choice for a soil application. High pH levels along with high calcium levels can precipitate boron out as calcium borate and limit its availability.

Liming soils may also temporarily reduce the availability of boron in the soil, even though the pH remains below 7.0. Boron is important for fertilization of the flowers and should be maximized during flowering by applying it as foliar feeding if necessary.

A water analysis should be performed to check the boron levels that are in irrigation water in order to prevent toxic accumulation of boron. Boron levels in a paste test at 1.0 ppm may be too high for some sensitive plants such as fruit trees.

## Iron

Iron should be greater than 50 ppm on the standard soil test, but lower values could be tolerated providing the pH is in the 6.5 range (or lower). I have never seen iron deficiency as a result of not having enough in the soil. Induced deficiencies because of liming or high bicarbonate levels in water seem to be the main reason for iron deficiencies in plants. We may have to choose between fixing the problem or merely treating the symptom. Recently glyphosate has been shown to tie up iron in glyphosate-tolerant crops, especially where the application is overlapped or used at high rates. If deficiencies do occur I would prefer to fix the problem by using foliar feeding.

## Manganese

Manganese should range between 40 and 80 ppm on the standard test. Manganese availability is very much affected by the pH and moisture level. Manganese is more soluble in moist conditions. This may mean that the plants don't have access to any more manganese, since root development could be limited. Figure 4 shows that most of the manganese in plants is picked up by diffusion and therefore needs a good root mass. Manganese may be more soluble and possibly more available during moist conditions, but this can rapidly change if the soils quickly dry out. High pH and well-aerated soils will exacerbate this problem.

As mentioned earlier, research by Dr. Huber and others on the effect of glyphosate on plants has shown that manganese availability can be substantially reduced as a result of the change glyphosate-tolerant genetics.

In northwest Ohio my tissue analyses typically indicate that I have about a 50% deficiency of manganese on both corn and bean crops. Repairing a manganese deficiency is best done through a foliar or starter application. After some experimental work that was done on my clients farms, I found that corn responded the best when manganese was foliar fed around the 5-6 leaf collar stage. This stage was too late for treating corn with only a zinc deficiency, but when both manganese and zinc deficiency occurred in the crop, spraying at the 5-6 leaf collar stage was best.

I have had some success in putting a good chelated manganese at 1.5 pints per acre in the starter fertilizer (placed 2 inches to the side and 2 inched below the seed) and then picking the results up in the tissue test. This has not been the case for zinc when the standard 1-2 pints per acre of a 6% chelated zinc is used.

## Copper

The recommended rate for copper should be between 3-5 ppm on the standard test. Copper is 10-100 times more available at a pH of 6 rather than at 7. As shown in Figure 4 most of the copper is picked up in plants by direct root intercept. This means that plants must have a good root mass in order to obtain enough copper.

Copper is important for nitrogen utilization and lignification in the plant. This is especially true for grasses where high nitrogen applications are being made. Based on Epstein's work in 1965, the ideal copper to nitrogen ratio is 1:2,500 in plants. It is not uncommon for me to see ratios of 1:7,000 in wheat tissue and 1:5,000 in corn tissue. With ratios this wide apart it is no wonder that we see poor nitrogen utilization and stand ability issues showing in the grass crops. A corrective treatment of copper sulfate can be use as a soil or foliar application. Foliar applications are generally limited to 1 pound of copper sulfate per acre. This has been done in the past more for its fungicidal properties and not so much as a foliar nutrient. Copper can act as a soil sterilant and care should be taken to keep the level below 20-25 ppm.

## Zinc

Zinc should range from 8-10 ppm on the standard test. Figure 4 shows that about 30% of zinc is picked up by direct root intercept and the rest is pulled from the solution in equal amounts by using mass flow and diffusion. Zinc is a trace element that is very difficult to get in adequate levels in the plant tissue, especially in the grasses. Farms receiving manures or biosolids are the exception to the rule.

In my tissue samples there seems to be a strong correlation between phosphorus uptake and the level of zinc. The lower the zinc level in the plant tissue, the lower the phosphorus level is in the tissue, even if the soil levels of phosphorus are adequate. I currently do not advocate trying to fix zinc deficiencies in crops solely through soil applications. I have applied a lot of zinc to the soil in the past and there is a lot of zinc still being applied to the soil today.

A six-year average of corn tissue between the 3-6 leaf collar stages averaged 88% deficient and the ear leaf tissues were 74% deficient. Wheat was 90% deficient at the pre-joint stage. A blend of broadcast, foliar feeding, and seed treatment may be what it takes to correct zinc deficiencies. Getting at least a half of a pound of zinc, applied early on growing crops such as corn and wheat, will satisfy most of the nutrient requirements for that year.

## Paste Analysis for High Exchange Capacity Soils

The paste analysis guidelines (Figure 34) for higher exchange capacity soils are not all that different from the low exchange capacity soils (Figure 10). The numbers can be somewhat lower since the higher exchange capacity soils have more buffering capacity. The soils themselves are holding more nutrients, therefore the flow rate of nutrients can be higher and more consistent. A soil holding more nutrients also means there are more cations such as calcium to interfere with nutrients such as phosphorus and boron. It is important to remember that higher nutrient holding capacity does not guarantee good solubility. The balance aspect is still important and should be maintained the same as the low exchange capacity soils.

The soil pH is still one of the key elements for maintaining nutrient solubility. Even if the pH drops into the upper 5s, don't be too quick to lime if the calcium solubility is good and phosphorus levels on the standard test are low. When you do lime, keep your applications of lime down to 2,000-3,000 lbs. per acre. It is not hard to cut your soluble phosphorus rates in half with a lime or even a gypsum application.

The next question you must ask yourself is, "Does the data on the standard test and/or solubility test truly reflect what's happening in the soil?" If lime was applied to the soil surface and not incorporated, then our core samples—which were collected and sent to the lab to be ground, mixed and analyzed—could very easily misrepresent the real situation in the soil. The higher the clay content of the soil, the more important incorporation becomes. This incorporation does not have to be an open invitation for soil erosion. Incorporating lime after wheat or early beans, followed by a secondary tillage pass and then followed by sowing a cover crop, can greatly reduce the erosion potential.

## Strategic Guidelines for High Exchange Capacity Soils When Using Paste Tests

|  | Desired Levels |
|---|---|
| Soil pH | 6.0-6.3 |
| Soluble Salts ppm | <1,200 |
| **Anions** | |
| Sulfur ppm | 5-6 |
| Chlorides ppm | <60 |
| Bicarbonates ppm | <90 |
| Phosphorus ppm | 0.3-0.4 |
| **Cations** | |
| Calcium ppm | 20-40 |
| Magnesium ppm | 4-8 |
| Potassium ppm | 10-12 |
| Sodium ppm | <5 |
| **Solution %** | |
| Calcium % | 60 |
| Magnesium % | 20 |
| Potassium % | 12-15 |
| Sodium % | <5 |
| **Trace Elements** | |
| Boron ppm | 0.05-0.10 |
| Iron ppm | 0.5-1.5 |
| Manganese ppm | 0.07-0.10 |
| Copper ppm | 0.05-0.08 |
| Zinc ppm | 0.07-0.15 |
| Aluminum ppm | <1.5 |

**Fig. 34** *This chart shows the strategic levels for nutrients when using the paste test for high exchanged capacity soils (TEC >10).*

# Chapter 5

# Interpretation of Soil Analysis Using Both Standard and Paste Tests

GETTING LOCKED INTO ONE APPROACH FOR BALANCING OR TREATING all soils is wrong. As in the previous chapters, the two soil types will be treated separately in this analysis. Soils with less than 10 exchange capacity (low) will be separated from those with an exchange capacity greater than 10 (high). The low exchange capacity soils will be balanced primarily using the SLAN (strategic level of available nutrients) method and the high exchange soils will be balanced using the BCSR (basic cation saturation ratio) method. Soils with exchange capacities that are two points away (plus or minus) from the cutoff point of 10 may be balanced using a combination of the two approaches.

When attempting to balance any soil for any crop, it is imperative to know the crop removal rates for at least phosphorus and potassium. Figure 11 shows the removal rates for corn, beans and wheat. There is a huge difference in nutrient removal when just the grain is removed compared to what is removed when addressing the grain and stover. Multiple cutting crops such as hay or turfgrass, where the clippings are not returned to the soil, remove large quantities of nutrients—especially potassium and calcium. Understanding the level of removal will allow an individual to adjust the fertilizer applications to include not only the removal but also to buildup nutrients.

The following soil balancing decision flowchart (Figure 35) shows the overall approach that I take to balance various soils. The low exchange capacity soils are balanced using the SLAN approach and the high exchange soils are balanced using the BCSR approach. Stopping the balance process with just using the standard test would be a grievous error, especially now that we have a paste test to use. The paste test could be used exclusively on the low exchange soils, except it is nice to know the level of reserve nutrients that could potentially come into solution—even on the heavier soils.

The low exchange capacity soils are always on the verge of either excess or deficiency, so having knowledge of the level of nutrients that have the potential to come into solution is powerful information. The trace elements, with the exception of boron, have been left out of the trace elements discussion for reasons mentioned in Chapter 3.

The remainder of this book will have soil examples and various resulting soil tests and contain my ideas of how best to balance the soils. The soil examples in this chapter and the next will be balanced using the standard test and also soil recommendations will be given for balancing using a combination of the standard and paste tests.

# Stratification Issues

Recently I received some soils data from a golf course that was having some problems. There were three greens sampled, at split depths. The samples were collected at 2 inches and 6 inches. I was a bit surprised at the level of stratification on these USGA greens. With actual exchange capacities being around 3, one would think that nutrients would move fairly well into the soil profile. Not so. Two of the greens had 70% of all the phosphorus in the top two inches, with the third having 60% in the top two inches. All three had nearly 60% of the potassium in the surface two inches. This is really not a problem for potassium and phosphorus uptake and movement in the plants as long as moisture is adequate. Phosphorus and potassium primarily move in the phloem of the plants, which allows it to move up or down where it is needed. For those with poor irrigation water, keeping the surface moist can create any number of issues from high salts to high bicarbonates.

My major concern with the split depth samples is the calcium levels. On two of the samples 60% of all the calcium was in the top two inches while the third sample was better with 40%. Calcium moves primarily upward through the xylem or water transport system. Therefore, calcium must be at the root tip in order to develop a good root system. The question becomes, "How do we develop a strong root system when the bulk of the calcium is at the surface?" The answer is "we can't." This current system encourages root development primarily at the surface, which leads to easy stress conditions from compaction and dry weather. Paste analysis showed that the surface 2 inches had met the threshold level of calcium, however the balance was over shadowed by the other cations.

The fix for this problem is not easy but it can be done. Deep core aeration and applying the appropriate calcium source immediately after aeration will help get calcium deeper in the profile. Testing the top dressing material with both the standard test and a paste test before application will help you adjust the top dress mix before it's applied.

*The Soil Probe Newsletter, Logan Labs*

There are hundreds of products which can be used to supply nutrients for the soil, however for simplicity I will use standard commercial products because of their consistency and high solubility. This does not mean that manures and organic products could not be used. Testing these products and equating them to the commercial products is quite acceptable. I would always rather balance soils using organic products if they are available and price competitive. Balancing with manures will generally result in elevated phosphorus levels in order to get enough potassium.

Pricing manures and biosolids is easy to do on a nutrient-by-nutrient basis, but putting a price on the organic matter value is anyone's guess. The only thing that I can guarantee is that there is a definite value for the organic matter. It is important to remember when buying organic products that once you exceed the level needed by the crop—especially in the anions such as sulfur and nitrogen—the value of that nutrient goes to zero. For example, chicken manure may have 15 lbs. per ton of available sulfur and consequently a ton and a half will supply the total crop needs, but if 3 tons per acre is applied, the sulfur in the last ton and a half has zero value. Keep this in mind when comparing organic fertilizers to commercial fertilizers. The commercial fertilizers have the benefit of being custom blended, but manures generally have one standard blend of nutrients.

# Soil Balancing Decision Flowchart

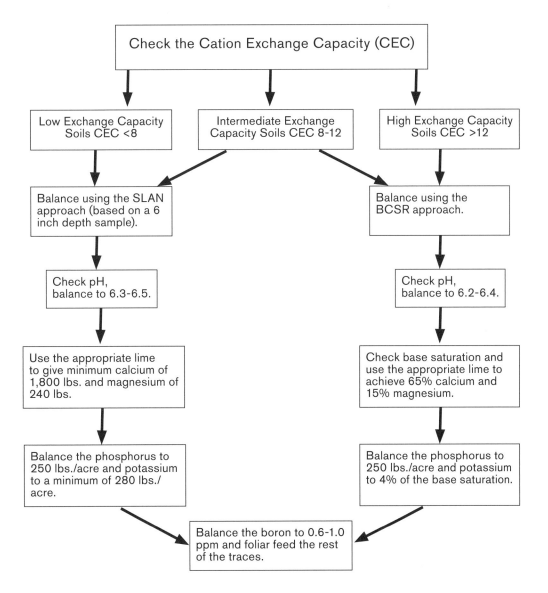

**Fig. 35** *The flowchart that the author uses to guide decision making and meet strategic nutrient levels for balancing soils.*

The following soil examples include the desired soil levels based on strategic nutrient levels or cation saturation percentages. The decision for this is based on the total exchange capacity (TEC) and as mentioned earlier the cutoff has been somewhat arbitrarily set at less than or greater than 10. Keep in mind the amounts of fertilizer that I suggest are not carved in stone and that they are also influenced by numerous tissue samples collected over the years. The following examples represent real soil testing situations.

## Low Exchange Capacity Soils Standard and Paste Test Example 1: Sample D-3

Looking at the standard soil report (Figure 36), the first thing I notice is the exchange capacity is below 10 and the sampling depth of 9 inches. This is a deep sampling depth and will have a substantial effect on the amount of nutrients needed to balance this soil sample. The low exchange capacity soil immediately causes my mind set to shift to the SLAN approach for balancing this soil. Next I look at the pH and see that it is below my desired level of 6.5.

Thinking about lime I look at the percentage of calcium and magnesium to decide what type of lime I should use. In this case the calcium and magnesium are both below my desired level on the percentage basis as well as the pounds per acre required. Therefore dolomitic lime is my lime of choice for starting the balancing process. I would correct the magnesium first with the dolomite lime and then switch to a calcium lime a year later if the calcium levels were not corrected with the dolomite lime.

The next question is how much lime should I apply? The decision is to use dolomite lime; so I would take the 227 lbs. per acre magnesium deficit and divide it by 220, which represents the pounds of magnesium in a ton of dolomite lime testing out at 11% magnesium. Therefore just over 1 ton of dolomite lime would satisfy my magnesium needs in the soil. This assumes that 100% of the lime will be dissolved and this is unlikely unless all the lime passes a 60-mesh screen. Most quarries test their product periodically and screen it for particle size. Sizes are generally separated into 8, 20, 60, and 100-mesh. This test quantifies how much of their lime will pass through each of the screens. 100-mesh means there is one hundred holes per square inch and 60-mesh means there is 60 holes per square inch and so on. The 60 and 100-mesh sizes are what I consider to be available for my soil amendment purposes. The 8 and 20 mesh sizes will become available sometime down the road, but not quickly or in large amounts. Therefore if the lime that I have available shows only 70% passing the 60-mesh screen then I will take the amount of lime required to balance my soil, in this case approximately 1.0 ton, and divide it by 0.7. This means that I would use 1.4 tons of dolomite lime per acre to correct my magnesium problem on this soil. This would not fix the calcium deficit and may not completely fix the magnesium deficit depending upon how much is tied up or fixed somewhere in the menagerie of soil chemical reactions.

For low exchange capacity soils, 4,000 lbs. per acre is the upper limit for adding lime at any one time. The balance cannot be achieved in one year without creating a massive imbalance in some other area of the soil nutrition equation. It has been my experience that soluble phosphorus on the paste test will be cut in half with the addition of any type of calcium such as lime or gypsum. In reality that is not likely to happen unless the lime is completely incorporated throughout the entire soil sampling depth. The goal is to monitor the soils frequently enough to prevent the need for a larger application of lime. In this example it would be a good idea to soil test prior to the next application of lime.

Some sort of tillage is very important in order to get lime to quickly and thoroughly react. For turfgrass this means core aeration prior to liming and also balancing the topdress to help compensate for any deficiencies. Lime applied to the surface will raise the pH in the immediate area to 7 or above, which will lower the solubility of the remaining lime to around 5% and slow the balancing process. This high pH zone will dramatically effect fertilizer applications. Not only will the solubility of nutrients such as phosphorus and the trace elements be reduced in the high pH zone, but also urea-based nitrogen's will be at risk of volatilization problems. Again the monitoring program needs to be done often enough to prevent the need for large applications. The low exchange capacity soils should be monitored at least on a yearly basis. Soils receiving irrigation should be monitored with a paste test mid-season after watering begins.

Liming low pH soils will result in a drop in the exchange capacity simply due to the fact that hydrogen ions, which take 20 lbs. per acre furrow slice (AFS) to make one milliequivalent, are being replaced by magnesium or calcium ions, which take 240 and 400 lbs. per acre furrow slice respectively to make one milliequivalent. This does not impact the desired levels for soils being balanced by the SLAN approach, but the high exchange capacity soils will see a drop in the desired levels since they are based on the exchange capacity. Consequently this phenomenon will give the appearance of having supplemented more nutrients than were really applied. The bottom line is that soil nutrient applications result in a change in the balance, and once equilibrium is achieved we start over by testing and rebalancing the new situation.

Balancing the potassium is not nearly as complicated as the calcium and magnesium. It is important to note that potassium sources such as potassium chloride and potassium sulfate are very soluble and can quickly overwhelm the solution and create a temporary imbalance. In our example this soil is deficient in potassium at a rate of 274 lbs. per acre. Since potassium on the soil report is listed as straight potassium and not $K_2O$, this number needs to be converted to $K_2O$ by dividing 274 by 0.82. This converts to a potassium deficit of 334 lbs. as $K_2O$. If we decide to use potassium chloride (which is 60% potassium as $K_2O$) as a means to balancing the soil, it would take nearly 600 lbs. (334/60=557) to satisfy the current deficit. If potassium sulfate were used instead of $K_2O$, then nearly 670 lbs. of material would be used. For a light soil this would be an overdose application and should be spread out over a couple of years. I would consider possibly applying 100-200 lbs. of potassium over my crop removal rate for any single year. High levels of potassium can compete with magnesium in the crop and create magnesium deficiencies. In the grasses, whether turf or general agriculture, additional luxury consumption of potassium can occur, potentially increasing your removal rate. Therefore, I prefer to make my large potassium applications in the fall for grasses, which will then take effect mainly the following year. A little extra potassium can't hurt over winter in turfgrass and winter wheat and will help reduce disease and winterkill.

Looking at the soil report (Figure 36), sulfur is low by 10-15 ppm and could be fixed in a number of ways. For crops needing nitrogen, ammonium sulfate (21-0-0-24) could be used. Adding 150 lbs. per acre of ammonium sulfate would contribute 36 lbs. of sulfur or 12 ppm on the 9 inch acre furrow slice (AFS). By taking the total depth of the soil sample and dividing it by 3 (9/3=3) and then using that number to divide into the number of pounds of sulfur applied with the ammonium sulfate (36/3=12), we can arrive at the parts per million of sulfur added. This is based on the assumption that every 3 inches per acre of soil weighs nearly 1,000,000 lbs.

Working the problem with K-Mag, which has 22% sulfur, is as follows. With a shortage of 15 ppm, multiply by 3 since the sample depth is nine inches (multiply by 2 if the sample depth is 6 inches) and the result is a need for 45 lbs. of sulfur. Since K-Mag is 22% sulfur we divide the 45 by 0.22 and end up needing to apply just over 200 lbs. of K-Mag to supply 15 ppm of sulfur.

Potassium sulfate and manures or biosolids could also be used as a source to supply sulfur. Elemental sulfur, despite being 90% sulfur, is not a good in season source of sulfur. This product is great for lowering pH, but requires biological activity to break the sulfur into the sulfate forms, so some lead time is needed to use this product. Since it is hard to predict the rate of breakdown, it is better to use sulfated forms of fertilizer as an in season sulfur source.

Phosphorus is 27 lbs. short of the desired level of 250 lbs. (Figure 34). Only 50 lbs. per acre of 11-52-0 (MAP) would be needed to fill the gap. Unfortunately adding the lime will certainly impact phosphorus availability and require additional applications. The other issue with phosphorus, which was alluded to earlier in this book, is the ease in which it is tied up, and it can be easily stratified. Phosphorus in soils is never what it seems. The paste test and ultimately tissue testing will need to be run in order to be confident of its availability. For a soil such as this, which is way out of balance, I would make many small applications of phosphorus for turfgrass and concentrate it in the band or starters for row crops.

Sodium in the solubility test looks very high at 22% (Figure 37). This is primarily the result of the lack of calcium, magnesium and potassium in the solution. The percentage of sodium will drop significantly once the other cations are brought up to threshold amounts and the balance is re-established.

The last area to be concerned with is the trace elements. Making a soil application of boron is one that I feel the most comfortable with at this time. As an anion, plants primarily pick up boron through mass flow (Figure 4). Boron on our soil test is 0.44 ppm (Figure 36) and I would prefer to have it closer to 0.6 ppm. Most of the soil-applied boron is approximately 10%. Therefore 15 lbs. of material blended with the other fertilizer and broadcasted would help fill this gap. I have blended up to 0.25 lbs. of actual boron with my 2" x 2" starter with no problems. I will admit this seems to make a lot of fertilizer dealers very uncomfortable.

Zinc and copper are very low on the soil report. A combination of soil broadcast and foliar feeding would be the best approach for these low levels. Cereal crops such as corn or wheat could be seed treated. Seed treatments are designed to be absorbed into the seed coat, which helps to limit the soil tieup issues. If I cannot foliar feed these products, then 5 lbs. per acre of copper sulfate and 10-20 lbs. per acre of zinc sulfate should be broadcast with the potassium and phosphorus. Stick to the sulfated forms of trace elements unless you have solubility data on the other products. Solubility can be an issue with the oxides or oxysulfate forms if you don't have a reputable source. Be sure to tissue test during the growing season to verify a response to your application.

For our soil example, the solubility test agrees nicely with the standard test and verifies how few of the available nutrients there really are in solution.

# Low Exchange Capacity Soils Standard Test
## Example 1: Sample D-3

| | | | D-3 |
|---|---|---|---|
| Sample Location | | | D-3 |
| Sample ID | | | |
| Lab Number | | | 23 |
| Sample Depth (inches) | | | 9 |
| Total Exchange Capacity (m.e.) | | | 4.42 |
| pH of Soil Sample | | | 5.30 |
| Organic Matter (percent) | | | 1.22 |
| Anions | SULFUR: | p.p.m. | 10 |
| | Mehlich III Phosphorus: | as ($P_2O_5$) lbs. / acre | 223 |
| Exchangeable Cations | CALCIUM: lbs. / acre | Value Found | 1134 |
| | MAGNESIUM: lbs. / acre | Value Found | 148 |
| | POTASSIUM: lbs. / acre | Value Found | 176 |
| | SODIUM: | lbs. / acre | 51 |
| Base Saturation % | Calcium (60 to 70%) | | 42.79 |
| | Magnesium (10 to 20%) | | 9.31 |
| | Potassium (2 to 5%) | | 3.41 |
| | Sodium (0.5 to 3%) | | 1.66 |
| | Other Bases (Variable) | | 6.80 |
| | Exchangeable Hydrogen (10 to 15%) | | 36.00 |
| Trace Elements | Boron (ppm) | | 0.44 |
| | Iron (ppm) | | 151 |
| | Manganese (ppm) | | 80 |
| | Copper (ppm) | | 0.68 |
| | Zinc (ppm) | | 1.08 |
| | Aluminum (ppm) | | 894 |

**Fig. 36** *Upon review, the first points of notice in this soil report are the deep sample depth of 9 inches, the total exchange capacity (6.63 m.e.) is under 10, and the pH (5.30) is below the desired 6.5 level. This is a deep sampling depth and will have a substantial effect on the amount of nutrients needed to balance this soil sample. The low exchange capacity soil should immediately cause a shift to the SLAN approach for balancing this soil.*

## Low Exchange Capacity Soils Paste Test
## Example 1: Sample D-3

| Sample Location | D-3 |
|---|---|
|  |  |
| Lab Number | 6360 |
| Water Used | DI |
|  |  |
| pH | 5.3 |
|  |  |
| Phosphorus | < 0.1 |
| Calcium | 1.9 |
| Magnesium | 0.5 |
| Potassium | 2.6 |
| Sodium | 1.4 |
| Sulfur | 0.6 |
|  |  |
| Boron | <0.02 |
| Iron | 1.03 |
| Manganese | 0.11 |
| Copper | < 0.02 |
| Zinc | < 0.02 |
| Aluminum | 2.33 |
| Molybdenum | < 0.01 |
| Cobalt | < 0.01 |
|  |  |
| Calcium % | 29.7% |
| Magnesium % | 7.3% |
| Potassium % | 41.1% |
| Sodium % | 22.0% |
|  |  |
| Calcium %:Magnesium % | 4.1 |
|  |  |
| Calcium mEq/L | 0.09 |
| Magnesium mEq/L | 0.16 |
| Potassium mEq/L | 0.05 |
| Sodium mEq/L | 0.09 |

**Fig. 37** *Sodium in this test looks very high at 22%. This is primarily the result of the lack of calcium, magnesium and potassium in the solution. The percentage of sodium (Na) will drop significantly once the other cations are brought up to threshold amounts and the balance is re-established.*

## Low Exchange Capacity Soils Standard Test Example 2: Turfgrass Samples 4 & 15

These are two very low exchange capacity soils which were initially sent in as turf samples. Whether turf or general agriculture these soils will almost certainly need irrigation to sustain viable plant growth unless rainfall comes quite frequently. The nutrient holding capacity is extremely low and will require in season applications of fertilizer. Since the nutrient-holding capacity is so low, crop requirements become more or less the strategic levels that we must provide if we are to grow a satisfactory crop. Growing turfgrass on this soil is much easier than growing a corn crop. A turfgrass crop will require a consistent flow of nutrients to maintain growth and color. Seed production crops such a corn have variable nutrient demand levels throughout the growing season. For example, almost all the potassium for a corn crop needs to be taken up in the plant by the time tasseling occurs. Front loading all the potassium prior to planting corn will certainly pressure magnesium and possibly calcium uptake. Note the amount of potassium required for the various crops in Figure 11. Crops grown on low exchange capacity soils need to be able to root below 12 inches to get moisture and nutrients. Any shallow restrictive layers will have far reaching ramifications on growth and yields. Another important factor is the quality of our irrigation water and how it might impact nutrient uptake (see Chapter 7).

The pH of the two soils for turfgrass is very high, so liming to adjust the pH is not an issue on these two samples. Sample 4 meets our strategic level of 1,200 lbs. per acre of calcium, however, Sample 15 is 219 lbs. short of the mark (Figure 38). Both samples are short of the 200 lbs. per acre magnesium level. Since the pH is high, magnesium needs to come from a source other than dolomite lime.

Further study of the reports indicates that sulfur and potassium are also short. This provides a great opportunity to use a product called K-Mag, formerly known as sul-po-mag. At 11% magnesium it would take 200 and 450 lbs. per acre to numerically satisfy the deficits on Samples 4 and 15 respectively. As with the potassium in the previous example, applying 450 lbs. per acre of K-Mag on Sample 15 would be an overload on the soil, not to mention an expensive proposition. By apply-ing 100-200 lbs. per acre of K-Mag over the removal rates, one could begin to head in the right direction. Our goals when applying nutrients is not to apply more nutrients than the crop can use or the soil can hold. When using K-Mag, which is roughly 22% sulfur, an application of 200 lbs. will supply the necessary sulfur for most crops, but only about two thirds of the needed magnesium. Applying K-Mag in excess of 200 lbs. will mean that the value of the sulfur in the K-Mag will go to zero. Since sulfur is an anion and not held in the soil it would be lost before the next crop was raised. This issue is minimal for cations, especially in the higher exchange capacity soils. Another option for magnesium would be to use a higher concentrated product like magnesium oxysulfate (36% Mg) at 40-60 lbs. and a potassium source in combination. Potassium chloride would be probably the cheapest source requiring 400-450 lbs. to satisfy the numerical deficiencies on this example, but again cause an overload on these light exchange capacity soils. Ammonium sulfate at 100 lbs. per acre would supply some nitrogen and the remaining sulfur. Finding the best combination for the best price requires some diligence.

Phosphorus is low in both samples but especially low in sample 15. With 250 lbs. per acre as our target it would take 64 lbs. and 138 lbs. of $P_2O_5$ on Samples 4 and 15 respectively. With the pH above 7, it would be best to use monoammonium phosphate (MAP), also referred to as 11-52-0 since the initial soil reaction is acidic. Dividing the deficits by 52, the amount of $P_2O_5$ in MAP, it would take 123 lbs. and 265 lbs. of 11-52-0 to meet the deficits for these two samples. Adding crop removal rates to each of these values again ends up with a large amount of material and large expense, as well as potential interference problems with zinc and other nutrients. Even if money were not an issue, phosphorus applied to the soil and not incorporated will result in stratification and environmental concerns. Remember that incorporation of all buildup applications will speed the soil balance process. Since incorporation also increases the risk of tie up, a combination of broadcast and row starter or foliar would be the best option. Besides minimizing stratification, nutrients will be more available during drought conditions since they will be deeper in the profile where there is moisture.

It is easy to see from this example that buildup applications should be made in the fall after the growing season is over. This will allow the soil chemistry to reach some sort of equilibrium before the next season. Multiple applications, heavy in the fall and light in the spring will ease the shock of nutrient applications. This is especially important on the low exchange capacity soils. It is in these light soils that manure and biosolid applications really shine. The nutrients are organically bound resulting in less interference issues, but the addition of organic matter is equally as important as the nutrients.

Boron and copper in this example are the two trace elements furthest from the requirements set in Figure 10. Applying 10 lbs. of 10% boron and 5 lbs. of copper sulfate in the broadcast with the major elements would be a good place to start for these traces. This should raise the boron by 0.5 ppm and the copper by 0.6 ppm in the soil, assuming no tie-ups or interferences. Retest the soil before adding any more trace elements. I cannot stress the fact enough that incorporation of fertilizer is a good idea. It is especially a good idea for a trace element like copper, since most of the uptake is by direct root intercept (Figure 4). If this were a no-till situation then I would opt for foliar feeding the copper over a soil application.

## Low Exchange Capacity Soils
## Standard Test Analysis, Example 2:
## Turfgrass Samples 4 & 15

| Sample Location | | | 4 | 15 |
|---|---|---|---|---|
| Sample ID | | | | |
| Lab Number | | | 54 | 57 |
| Sample Depth (inches) | | | 6 | 6 |
| Total Exchange Capacity (m.e.) | | | 4.12 | 3.30 |
| pH of Soil Sample | | | 7.40 | 7.60 |
| Organic Matter (percent) | | | 1.91 | 1.41 |
| Anions | SULFUR: | p.p.m. | 4 | 4 |
| | Mehlich III Phosphorus: | as ($P_2O_5$) lbs. / acre | 186 | 112 |
| Exchangeable Cations | CALCIUM: lbs. / acre | Desired Value | 1200 | 1200 |
| | | Value Found | 1241 | 981 |
| | | Deficit | | -219 |
| | MAGNESIUM: lbs. / acre | Desired Value | 200 | 200 |
| | | Value Found | 178 | 150 |
| | | Deficit | -22 | -50 |
| | POTASSIUM: lbs. / acre | Desired Value | 220 | 220 |
| | | Value Found | 46 | 37 |
| | | Deficit | -174 | -183 |
| | SODIUM: | lbs. / acre | 26 | 22 |
| Base Saturation % | Calcium (60 to 70%) | | 75.25 | 74.34 |
| | Magnesium (10 to 20%) | | 17.99 | 18.94 |
| | Potassium (2 to 5%) | | 1.43 | 1.44 |
| | Sodium (0.5 to 3%) | | 1.36 | 1.42 |
| | Other Bases (Variable) | | 4.00 | 3.80 |
| | Exchangeable Hydrogen (10 to 15%) | | 0.00 | 0.00 |
| Trace Elements | Boron (ppm) | | 0.51 | 0.46 |
| | Iron (ppm) | | 148 | 94 |
| | Manganese (ppm) | | 66 | 69 |
| | Copper (ppm) | | 0.93 | 0.96 |
| | Zinc (ppm) | | 4.18 | 6.48 |
| | Aluminum (ppm) | | 63 | 64 |

**Fig. 38** *Sample 4 meets our strategic level of 1,200 lbs. per acre of calcium, however Sample 15 is 219 lbs. short of the mark.*

## Low Exchange Capacity Soils Paste Test
## Example 2: Turfgrass Samples 4 & 15

In this example the paste analysis will be evaluated in conjunction with the previous standard analysis. What we will find is that some nutrition levels are better and some are worse than what appeared in the standard test. It is important to remember that with the paste analysis it is necessary that we look not only at threshold amounts but the balance in the solution. It is quite possible to have a great balance and not have enough total nutrients in solution to sustain maximum growth.

The pH level (Figure 39) in the paste test is high as it is in the standard soil report (Figure 38). Skipping down the report, the calcium is just below the desired level and the magnesium is in excellent shape. Notice that the sample with the highest level of soluble calcium had the lowest value found on the standard report. There is *no consistent correlation* between the standard test and the paste test. The unknown aspect about the paste test is the feed rate. The feed rate is the speed that nutrients will dissolve or come off the colloid into solution. Just because the report shows adequate levels of the nutrient, will those nutrients once pulled from the solution by the plant or flushed by a heavy rain recover fast enough and often enough to satisfy the crops needs during the growing season? This is truly an unknown, but data from the standard test will help make the decision much easier. The feeding of nutrients into solution primarily comes from the exchange sites on the soil colloid. Certainly nutrients will enter the solution when organic matter is degraded, but that is much more uncertain than the level of nutrients reported on the standard test. Since low exchange capacity soils do not have a large number of exchange sites, flow rates must always be suspect. Having a low exchange capacity soil with deficiencies on the standard test should certainly raise a red flag concerning feed rate. An analogy for flow rate would be a rain barrel with a hose attached at the bottom. As long as the rain barrel is full, the flow of water from the hose will be high, however, as the barrel empties out the flow of water from the hose will decrease. Those nutrients on the standard test represent the potential of the rain barrel. A soil with a standard soil test that has no nutrient deficits would represent a full barrel and a high potential flow rate. Currently there is no standard method set up to measure flow rate. It could be estimated by repeated paste testing and plotting the reduction of nutrients in solution. This would be an estimate at best since flow rates will be a function of many factors such as microbial activity, temperature and plant types. Tissue sampling is the best way to indirectly measure flow rate against demand.

If the nutrient levels are good in both the standard test and the paste test, I feel fairly confident that the feed rate will be good too. In this example, the calcium is good enough in both tests that I feel the feed rate will be good enough for at least this season. If the calcium in the paste test had been less than 15 ppm, I would have considered using some gypsum as my soluble source of calcium. The crop will also have an influence on my decision based on the demand of nutrients it has during the growing season. For example, if I were growing alfalfa on this soil, which has a very high removal rate for calcium and potassium, I would have to decide whether these light soils could withstand the draw down. I would soil test soils with this low of exchange capacity on a yearly basis.

The magnesium in this example, although good in solubility, is low on the standard test therefore putting the feed rate in jeopardy. I would maintain my application of K-Mag or some other source. Potassium is low on both tests substantiating the need for a gradual buildup and maintenance applications.

The trace element results on the paste test would cause me to abandon the boron broadcast in lieu of a foliar application since the solubility of boron is at the upper limit. I would still broadcast copper as well as foliar feed copper along with zinc.

Aluminum and iron will sometimes appear to be very high on the paste test. Unless the pH is very low I would not be too concerned with this. Clay particles are extremely small and occasionally slip past the filter paper in the extraction process and get vaporized in the ICP unit and turned into their primary elements of aluminum and iron.

# Low Exchange Capacity Soils
## Paste Test Analysis, Example 2:
## Turfgrass Samples 4 & 15

| Sample Location | | | 4 | 15 |
|---|---|---|---|---|
| | | | | |
| Lab Number | | | 17465 | 17466 |
| Water Used | | | DI | DI |
| pH | | | 7.4 | 7.6 |
| Soluble Salts | | ppm | 120 | 51 |
| Chloride (Cl) | | ppm | 9 | 9 |
| Bicarbonate ($HCO_3$) | | ppm | 134 | 173 |
| Anions | SULFUR | ppm | 1.75 | 2.58 |
| | PHOSPHORUS | ppm | < 0.1 | < 0.1 |
| Soluble Cations | CALCIUM | ppm | 23.13 | 29.85 |
| | | meq/l | 1.16 | 1.49 |
| | MAGNESIUM | ppm | 6.35 | 7.62 |
| | | meq/l | 0.53 | 0.64 |
| | POTASSIUM | ppm | 9.42 | 8.01 |
| | | meq/l | 0.24 | 0.21 |
| | SODIUM | ppm | 4.66 | 4.64 |
| | | meq/l | 0.20 | 0.20 |
| Percent | Calcium | | 54.23 | 58.82 |
| | Magnesium | | 24.81 | 25.03 |
| | Potassium | | 11.47 | 8.20 |
| | Sodium | | 9.49 | 7.95 |
| Trace Elements | Boron (ppm) | | 0.1 | 0.1 |
| | Iron (ppm) | | 2.57 | 1.42 |
| | Manganese (ppm) | | 0.18 | 0.18 |
| | Copper (ppm) | | < 0.02 | < 0.02 |
| | Zinc (ppm) | | < 0.02 | < 0.02 |
| | Aluminum (ppm) | | 3.43 | 1.88 |

**Fig. 39** *The pH level in the paste test is high in the paste test as it is in the standard soil report. Also calcium is just below the desired level, but the magnesium is in excellent shape.*

## Low Exchange Capacity Soils Standard Test
## Example 3: Coastal

This is another low exchange capacity soil with a pH just a little under our desired level of 6.5. Both the calcium and magnesium in the soil are a little short by my standards, but the potassium is very low at 129 lbs. below the labs desired level. For a heavy potassium feeder like coastal Bermuda grass, these levels will not last long. The pH is a measure of hydrogen ion concentration, but it is affected by the other cations in the soil. Since the pH is a little low, adding potassium to the soil could bring the pH up right in line with the desired level once equilibrium is reached. To fix this deficit it would take 160 lbs. of $K_2O$, which is equivalent to approximately 262 lbs. of muriate of potash. This assumes none of the potassium is getting fixed in the soil, which is unlikely. Meeting the removal rates and adding 150-200 lbs. extra over time would bring the soils into a better balanced situation. The sulfur is very low so using 150 lbs. of potassium sulfate as part of your potassium source, or 125 lbs. of ammonium sulfate if nitrogen is needed for the crop, would provide the necessary sulfur.

Phosphorus is extremely low, almost to the point of being non-existent. Since this soil is acidic, rock phosphate could be used to build the phosphorus level in the soil, unless this is a pasture or no-till situation. An application of finely ground 100- to 200-mesh rock phosphate could be applied if it is available. In the past I have used Florida rock phosphate very successfully in this situation. The applications were generally in the 1,000 lbs. per acre range because that was as low as the equipment would spread. Special spreading equipment had to be used because of the fineness of the product. It is the extreme fineness that allows this low solubility product to work. Along with the rock phosphate application one also gets calcium and a lot of trace elements. The rock phosphate does not create the interference problems with other elements that we get when using the commercial grade fertilizers. I would avoid using rock phosphate if I couldn't do some tillage or if working on rented ground that I wasn't sure I would have for 6-8 years. If commercial grade fertilizers are all that are available, diammonium phosphate (DAP), also referred to as 18-46-0, would be the phosphorus source of choice. Unlike MAP, which has an acidic initial reaction, DAP has a basic initial reaction. An application of 460 lbs. per acre of DAP would be needed to satisfy the numerical deficits on the soil report. Again this is too much for a one-time application, but spread out over time along with considering crop removal rates, these applications would go a long way to eliminate the deficits.

The boron level is a little short, but the copper and zinc levels are about as low as they can get. Based on this analysis alone I would add 10 lbs. of 10% boron, 5 lbs. of copper sulfate, and 15 lbs. of zinc sulfate, all blended and broadcasted with my potassium and phosphate fertilizer. I would prefer to see this material tilled into the soil to a depth of 6 to 9 inches.

## Low Exchange Capacity Soils Standard Test
## Example 3: Coastal

| Sample Location | | | Coastal |
|---|---|---|---|
| | | | |
| Lab Number | | | 119 |
| Sample Depth (inches) | | | 8 |
| Total Exchange Capacity (m.e.) | | | 5.82 |
| pH of Soil Sample | | | 6.10 |
| Organic Matter (percent) | | | 0.68 |
| **Anions** SULFUR: | p.p.m. | | < 3 |
| Mehlich III Phosphorus: | as ($P_2O_5$) lbs. / acre | | 37 |
| **Exchangeable Cations** CALCIUM: lbs. / acre | Desired Value | | 2111 |
| | Value Found | | 1982 |
| | Deficit | | -129 |
| MAGNESIUM: lbs. / acre | Desired Value | | 223 |
| | Value Found | | 267 |
| | Deficit | | |
| POTASSIUM: lbs. / acre | Desired Value | | 242 |
| | Value Found | | 113 |
| | Deficit | | -129 |
| SODIUM: | lbs. / acre | | 45 |
| **Base Saturation %** Calcium (60 to 70%) | | | 63.84 |
| Magnesium (10 to 20%) | | | 14.33 |
| Potassium (2 to 5%) | | | 1.87 |
| Sodium (0.5 to 3%) | | | 1.25 |
| Other Bases (Variable) | | | 5.20 |
| Exchangeable Hydrogen (10 to 15%) | | | 13.50 |
| **Trace Elements** Boron (ppm) | | | 0.43 |
| Iron (ppm) | | | 73 |
| Manganese (ppm) | | | 58 |
| Copper (ppm) | | | 0.42 |
| Zinc (ppm) | | | 0.52 |
| Aluminum (ppm) | | | 429 |

**Fig. 40** *The pH just a little under our desired level of 6.5. Both the calcium and magnesium is a little short, but the potassium is very low at 287 pounds below the desired level. The phosphorus is extremely low almost being non-existent. Since this soil is acidic, rock phosphate could be used to build the phosphorus level.*

## Low Exchange Capacity Soils Paste Test
## Example 3: Coastal

This paste analysis is just about as poor as it gets. Many aspects of this sample can be summed up with three words "slim to none." The calcium and magnesium on the standard report doesn't really look too bad; however, the paste test is 180 degrees in the opposite direction. There is virtually no calcium or magnesium in solution. The phosphorus on the standard test is very low and it is below the Logan Labs instrumentation's detection limit on the paste test. There is a little bit of potassium in solution, but still about 30% of what it should be. The balance of calcium and magnesium percentages is reversed. The sodium appears to be a real problem with 35% of all the nutrients in solution being sodium. Possibly the only bright spot is the trace elements, which appear to be much better in the paste test than the standard test (with the exception of copper). The fix for this soil is much different when the paste test is considered. You might even question the validity of the paste test until you talk to the owner of this soil and he describes the multitude of problems he was having with his dairy cows.

The phosphorus recommendations would remain the same as those presented in the standard test evaluation. This soil also needs a lot of soluble calcium and magnesium. The sodium is not really a problem in the soil. The high percentage in solution is the result of the extremely low levels of soluble calcium and magnesium in solution. Fix the calcium and magnesium problem and the sodium will go away on its own. I would start by broadcasting 800-1,000 lbs. of bulk gypsum in order to get the calcium and sulfur that the soil needs. Three to four hundred pounds of gypsum might maintain the soluble levels down the road, but additional testing a year later should be done to verify the need. I would plan on testing this soil at least three years in a row until the nutrient profile begins to stabilize.

The potassium recommendations would be much the same as in the standard evaluation except for the use of K-Mag. Ignoring the magnesium could lead to a real grass tetany problem in cattle. The gypsum would supply the sulfur, and unless I could not get another reasonably priced source of magnesium such as magnesium sulfate or magnesium oxysulfate, I would still use the K-Mag at 200-250 lbs. per acre. Since it is hard to comprehend the overall soil reaction in this complex situation, many of the recommendations will simply be experimental, hence the need for yearly soil testing. It is quite possible that once the gypsum reacts in the soil, more magnesium will become available reducing or even eliminating the need for K-Mag. The standard test suggests that there is not a lot of magnesium on the colloid, so I would stay with the initial rates.  Applying gypsum and commercial grade phosphorus is somewhat antagonistic. Soluble phosphorus can react very quickly with calcium and form rock phosphate. It is not uncommon to see the soluble phosphorus cut in half whenever a calcium source is applied. This becomes a necessary tradeoff since the calcium is critical for root development. If we can increase the root mass, this will elevate the availability of all nutrients and ultimately increase biological activity through higher levels of organic residue. Remember balancing soils is not a short trip but rather a journey.

With the solubility test in hand, I would make some changes in the minor element program. First I would drop the boron broadcast but keep the copper and zinc. However, I might hold off on the copper and zinc application for six months until the soil reaches equilibrium from the gypsum, phosphorus and potassium buildup applications, which hopefully would preferably be done in the fall. Foliar feed the copper and zinc until a followup soil sample 6-12 months later can be taken. Delaying the trace element applications would also apply if rock phosphate were used as a buildup since it does contain many trace elements.

# Low Exchange Capacity Soils Paste Test
## Example 3: Coastal

| Sample Location | | | Coastal |
|---|---|---|---|
| | | | |
| Lab Number | | | 16678 |
| Water Used | | | DI |
| pH | | | 6.1 |
| Soluble Salts | | ppm | 17 |
| Chloride (Cl) | | ppm | 3 |
| Bicarbonate (HCO$_3$) | | ppm | 22 |
| Anions | SULFUR | ppm | 0.55 |
| | PHOSPHORUS | ppm | < 0.1 |
| Soluble Cations | CALCIUM | ppm | 1.82 |
| | | meq/l | 0.09 |
| | MAGNESIUM | ppm | 2.3 |
| | | meq/l | 0.19 |
| | POTASSIUM | ppm | 4.86 |
| | | meq/l | 0.13 |
| | SODIUM | ppm | 5.18 |
| | | meq/l | 0.23 |
| Percent | Calcium | | 14.37 |
| | Magnesium | | 30.24 |
| | Potassium | | 19.90 |
| | Sodium | | 35.49 |
| Trace Elements | Boron (ppm) | | 0.1 |
| | Iron (ppm) | | 8.78 |
| | Manganese (ppm) | | 0.19 |
| | Copper (ppm) | | < 0.02 |
| | Zinc (ppm) | | 0.05 |
| | Aluminum (ppm) | | 1.7 |

**Fig. 41** *This paste analysis of this soil sample is just about as poor as it gets. There is virtually no calcium or magnesium in solution and the phosphorus is below the level that the testing instruments can detect (<0.1 ppm).*

## Low Exchange Capacity Soils Standard Test Example 4: South

This is another low exchange capacity soil with a very high pH (Figure 43). This soil is almost pure sand with virtually no organic matter and consequently no buffering or nutrient-holding capacity. Many golf course greens and tees have these types of soil conditions. Drainage is not generally an issue, but applying nutrients in the right quantities and at the right time is a real challenge. This soil sample along with the previous low exchange capacity samples would benefit from multiple applications done pre-season and in season. There is practically no holding capacity and many of the nutrients measured in the lab probably are not on the colloid. It is very difficult to balance and hold the balance on these soils. Attempting to balance these soils is like walking down a three-foot-wide path with a hundred foot dropoff on each side; if you stumble the results could be disastrous. Soil testing, especially paste testing, is absolutely critical in order to have enough information to stay on the path.

This soil shows very low sulfur, phosphorus and potassium for the major elements. Boron, copper and zinc are low for the minor elements.

When the pH gets over 7.3 the Mehlich extracting solution, which has a pH of 2.5, may start to get neutralized and fail to pick up all the phosphorus. The phosphorus number on this test is very low and the pH very high; therefore, the phosphorus value should be suspect unless another test is used to verify the value. A phosphorus test known as the Olsen can be used to verify if the Mehlich extracted phosphorus is being impacted by the high pH. Values >17 on the Olsen test would equate to a 250 lb. value found on the Mehlich test. The paste test could also be used to see if there is adequate phosphorus in solution. After all, water-soluble phosphorus is really what is best for the plants.

Since the sulfur is low and the pH is so high, an application of elemental sulfur could fix both problems and reduce the impact on phosphorus. The following chart taken from the *Knott's Handbook for Vegetable Growers* is what I follow in order to adjust soil pH downward.

## Estimated Quantities of Sulfur
## Needed to Lower pH

| | 90% Sulfur (lbs./acre) | | |
| --- | --- | --- | --- |
| pH Change Desired | Sand | Loam | Clay |
| from 8.5 to 6.5 | 2,000 | 2,500 | 3,000 |
| from 8.0 to 6.5 | 1,200 | 1,500 | 2,000 |
| from 7.5 to 6.5 | 500 | 800 | 1,000 |
| from 7.0 to 6.5 | 100 | 150 | 300 |

**Fig. 42** *Estimated quantities of 90% sulfur needed to lower the soil pH from 8.5 to 6.5. Data from* Knott's Handbook for Vegetable Growers *by Oscar Lorenz and Donald Maynard.*

Depending on the source and cost this may or may not be practical. For a small acreage of greens and tees on a golf course it may work, but I would not try to make the adjustment all at one time. Elemental sulfur is broken down by biological activity, so the pH reduction will take some time depending upon the degree of mixing and the biological populations. Incorporation is important so as not to create a low pH zone on the surface. The pH will drop over time with nitrogen applications, especially if ammonium sulfate is used.

The potassium level on this test (Figure 43) is very low requiring exorbitant amounts of this nutrient. Applying 100-200 lbs. per acre of potassium chloride or potassium sulfate *over the removal rates* would be a start in the right direction. Potassium is so important for water utilization, disease resistance and carbohydrate movement that every effort needs to be made to build it up, but care must be taken not to block magnesium uptake.

Boron, copper and zinc are all low on the standard test (Figure 43). The pH is so high that it might be fruitless to broadcast the deficient trace elements unless they can be blended with something like ammonium sulfate, which is very acidifying. Tissue testing should follow thereafter to see if the trace element availability is enhanced. Foliar feeding would be the most effective method of getting the trace nutrients into the plant. The rates and timing would depend on the type of products being used. On turf crops, which are frequently mown, it would be better if chelates or water-soluble sulfates were used since they would enter the plant quickly and be mobilized easily.

For general agricultural crops I really like the flowable formulations that have a high concentration of metals which are ground into 2-10 micron sizes. The particle size variation seems to allow trace metals to enter the plant over a longer period of time. I have had clients spray corn at the 5-leaf collar stage with flowable products and then monitored the tissues weekly until physiological maturity. The trace elements maintained excellent levels over the entire season. Some of these products weigh as much as 15 lbs. per gallon, which contain enough trace metal in one pint of material to spray a half a pound of metal per acre.

Due to the high concentration of metal trace elements in these products they do not stay in suspension very well if left to stand for any length of time. When these products are mixed they should be sprayed right away and followed with a thorough rinsing of the sprayer. I find these products quite effective and at a relatively low cost in comparison to the chelates. The chelates on the other hand are easier to mix and stay in suspension better. Both types of products are excellent but require different budgets and management styles.

# Low Exchange Capacity Soils Standard Test
## Example 4: South

| Sample Location | | | South |
|---|---|---|---|
| | | | |
| Lab Number | | | 58 |
| Sample Depth (inches) | | | 6 |
| Total Exchange Capacity (m.e.) | | | 5.14 |
| pH of Soil Sample | | | 8.10 |
| Organic Matter (percent) | | | 0.38 |
| Anions | SULFUR: | p.p.m. | 4 |
| | Mehlich III Phosphorus: | as ($P_2O_5$) lbs. / acre | 54 |
| Exchangeable Cations | CALCIUM: lbs. / acre | Desired Value | 1336 |
| | | Value Found | 1527 |
| | | Deficit | |
| | MAGNESIUM: lbs. / acre | Desired Value | 200 |
| | | Value Found | 248 |
| | | Deficit | |
| | POTASSIUM: lbs. / acre | Desired Value | 220 |
| | | Value Found | 53 |
| | | Deficit | -167 |
| | SODIUM: | lbs. / acre | 21 |
| Base Saturation % | Calcium (60 to 70%) | | 74.33 |
| | Magnesium (10 to 20%) | | 20.12 |
| | Potassium (2 to 5%) | | 1.32 |
| | Sodium (0.5 to 3%) | | 0.90 |
| | Other Bases (Variable) | | 3.30 |
| | Exchangeable Hydrogen (10 to 15%) | | 0.00 |
| Trace Elements | Boron (ppm) | | 0.36 |
| | Iron (ppm) | | 127 |
| | Manganese (ppm) | | 48 |
| | Copper (ppm) | | 1.22 |
| | Zinc (ppm) | | 0.58 |
| | Aluminum (ppm) | | 289 |

**Fig. 43** *This example has a very high pH. The soil is almost pure sand with virtually no organic matter and consequently no buffering or nutrient-holding capacity. There is practically no holding capacity and many of the nutrients measured in the lab probably are not on the soil colloid. This soil shows very low sulfur, phosphorus and potassium for the major elements. Boron, copper and zinc are low for the minor elements.*

## Low Exchange Capacity Soils Paste Test
## Example 4: South

The paste test verifies that the phosphorus is still available in solution and suggests that the high pH may be affecting the Mehlich extracting solution used in the standard test. This fact would not prevent me from applying removal rates of phosphorus after harvest. The calcium and magnesium levels in the paste test are mediocre to low. This sample appears to have been limed prior to being sampled and the soils may still be trying to reach equilibrium. Remember, the solubility of even the best grade of lime will drop to 5-10% when the pH of the solution rises above 7. Consequently, I would not be interested in applying any additional soluble calcium and magnesium, but instead I would try to increase the incorporation and wait to see if the sulfur or ammonium sulfate additions would further enhance the breakdown and increase the amount of soluble calcium and magnesium available. If the solubility of calcium and magnesium is not improved by next time the soil is sampled, then steps should be taken to increase the solubility of the cations.

The potassium in this sample is very low in solution, but with the addition of potassium sulfate or chloride this level will rapidly increase due to the solubility of the products. Also, the results show that the sodium is high on a percentage basis, but as in the previous example it is only high because the other cations are low.

Boron, copper and zinc are all below the ICP's detection limit (<0.02 ppm). I would forego any broadcast of trace elements based on this data and apply the trace elements which are deficient as a foliar application as discussed above.

## Low Exchange Capacity Soils Paste Test
## Example 4: South

| Sample Location | | | Pinwheel |
|---|---|---|---|
| Sample Id | | | South |
| Lab Number | | | 14994 |
| Water Used | | | DI |
| pH | | | 8.1 |
| Soluble Salts | ppm | | 61 |
| Chloride (Cl) | ppm | | 22 |
| Bicarbonate (HCO$_3$) | ppm | | 63 |
| Anions | SULFUR | ppm | 0.71 |
| | PHOSPHORUS | ppm | 0.55 |
| Soluble Cations | CALCIUM | ppm | 13.45 |
| | | meq/l | 0.67 |
| | MAGNESIUM | ppm | 3.28 |
| | | meq/l | 0.27 |
| | POTASSIUM | ppm | 2.86 |
| | | meq/l | 0.07 |
| | SODIUM | ppm | 3.18 |
| | | meq/l | 0.14 |
| Percent | Calcium | | 58.07 |
| | Magnesium | | 23.58 |
| | Potassium | | 6.41 |
| | Sodium | | 11.95 |
| Trace Elements | Boron (ppm) | | < 0.02 |
| | Iron (ppm) | | 3.91 |
| | Manganese (ppm) | | 0.13 |
| | Copper (ppm) | | < 0.02 |
| | Zinc (ppm) | | < 0.02 |
| | Aluminum (ppm) | | 5.32 |

**Fig. 44** *This paste test verifies that the phosphorus is still available in solution and that the calcium and magnesium levels are mediocre to low. This sample appears to have been limed prior to being sampled and the soils may still be trying to reach equilibrium. The potassium is very low in solution. Boron, copper and zinc are all below the testing equipment's detection limit.*

## Low Exchange Capacity Soils Standard Test Example 5: Golf Course Green Sample 14

This sample is a low exchange capacity soil sent in from a golf course green. The pH is high but not excessive. The soil has very little organic matter yielding little water-holding or nutrient-holding or buffering capacity. The standard test shows that the sulfur level is good and the phosphorus is high, but the magnesium is low and the potassium is very low. The trace elements are good, with copper being the exception at about half the amount it should be. This sample appears to have been limed with a high calcium lime when in fact a dolomite lime should have been used. A good starting point for potassium is to use K-Mag at 250 lbs. per acre or 6 lbs. per 1,000 ft$^2$ along with 150-200 lbs. per acre or 4.5 lbs. per 1,000 ft$^2$ of potassium over the removal rates.

On these light soils I would recommend keeping the K-Mag in the broadcast as long as you are adding a straight potassium product. A large application of just potassium could be made during the fall or winter months for buildup purposes.

The phosphorus is very high and it appears as though we could go a few years without making any phosphorus applications. The trace elements are high enough that I would not make any broadcast applications based on this data.

## Low Exchange Capacity Soils Standard Test
## Example 5: Golf Course Green Sample 14

| | | | Green |
|---|---|---|---|
| Sample Location | | | Green |
| Sample ID | | | 14 |
| Lab Number | | | 6 |
| Sample Depth (inches) | | | 6 |
| Total Exchange Capacity (m.e.) | | | 6.67 |
| pH of Soil Sample | | | 7.20 |
| Organic Matter (percent) | | | 0.49 |
| Anions | SULFUR: | p.p.m. | 24 |
| | Mehlich III Phosphorus: | as (P$_2$O$_5$) lbs. / acre | 463 |
| Exchangeable Cations | CALCIUM: lbs / acre | Desired Value | 1812 |
| | | Value Found | 2196 |
| | | Deficit | |
| | MAGNESIUM: lbs. / acre | Desired Value | 200 |
| | | Value Found | 171 |
| | | Deficit | -29 |
| | POTASSIUM: lbs. / acre | Desired Value | 207 |
| | | Value Found | 87 |
| | | Deficit | -120 |
| | SODIUM: | lbs. / acre | 33 |
| Base Saturation % | Calcium (60 to 70%) | | 82.37 |
| | Magnesium (10 to 20%) | | 10.69 |
| | Potassium (2 to 5%) | | 1.67 |
| | Sodium (0.5 to 3%) | | 1.07 |
| | Other Bases (Variable) | | 4.20 |
| | Exchangeable Hydrogen (10 to 15%) | | 0.00 |
| Trace Elements | Boron (ppm) | | 0.69 |
| | Iron (ppm) | | 116 |
| | Manganese (ppm) | | 31 |
| | Copper (ppm) | | 1.38 |
| | Zinc (ppm) | | 7.62 |
| | Aluminum (ppm) | | 409 |

**Fig. 45** *This soil has very little organic matter yielding little water-holding or nutrient-holding or buffering capacity. The sulfur level is good and the phosphorus is high (not needing any more for several years). The magnesium is low and the potassium is very low.*

## Low Exchange Capacity Soils Paste Test
## Example 5: Golf Course Green Sample 14

The paste analysis for this soil sample paints a somewhat differ-ent picture than what we saw with the standard test. The calcium and phosphorus levels are low in spite of the good results for them on the standard test. Magnesium is low, but about where one might expect it to be, and the potassium is higher than expected. The trace elements are all low with the exception of iron. Since the organic matter is so low, biological activity could be nearly nonexistent and not making any contribution to solubilizing nutrients.

I would apply a starter fertilizer or a pop-up to this soil if growing row crops. The starter might consist of an application of 5 gallons per acre of an orthophosphate or polyphosphate fertilizer. Soybeans, wheat or turf would get an application of a 3-20-20 type of foliar fertilizer—especially under cold conditions and during critical times around flowering. With the high levels of phosphate on the standard test, it is not important to build phosphorus levels, but just maintain and enhance their availability. Microbial populations improve phospho-rus solubility. This soil has very little organic matter so applying some dry humate products at 10-12 lbs. per acre or applying manures could improve the biological conditions in the soil.

I would attempt to improve the calcium solubility through acidic nitrogen applications and organic additions. Another suggestion is to also go back and see what the screen mesh size was on the lime that was previously used. If 50-60% of the lime did *not* pass the 60-mesh screen and the lime had been on for more than a year, then I might consider using a soluble calcium source like gypsum after the potassium and magnesium were adjusted.

The paste test, like the standard test, shows that K-Mag would be a good fit for this soil. Some additional potassium could be used following the K-Mag application.

A multiple trace element package with boron, manganese, copper and zinc should be sprayed on to cover the solubility deficits.

# Low Exchange Capacity Soils Paste Test
## Example 5: Golf Course Green Sample 14

| | | | Green |
|---|---|---|---|
| Sample Location | | | Green |
| Sample Id | | | 14 |
| Lab Number | | | 12003 |
| Water Used | | | DI |
| pH | | | 7.2 |
| Soluble Salts | | ppm | 216 |
| Chloride (Cl) | | ppm | 5 |
| Bicarbonate (HCO$_3$) | | ppm | 93 |
| Anions | SULFUR | ppm | 2.28 |
| | PHOSPHORUS | ppm | 0.12 |
| Soluble Cations | CALCIUM | ppm | 19.93 |
| | | meq/l | 1.00 |
| | MAGNESIUM | ppm | 3.17 |
| | | meq/l | 0.26 |
| | POTASSIUM | ppm | 7.06 |
| | | meq/l | 0.18 |
| | SODIUM | ppm | 3.01 |
| | | meq/l | 0.13 |
| Percent | Calcium | | 63.27 |
| | Magnesium | | 16.78 |
| | Potassium | | 11.65 |
| | Sodium | | 8.30 |
| Trace Elements | Boron (ppm) | | < 0.02 |
| | Iron (ppm) | | 4.25 |
| | Manganese (ppm) | | 0.03 |
| | Copper (ppm) | | 0.02 |
| | Zinc (ppm) | | 0.02 |
| | Aluminum (ppm) | | 9.08 |

**Fig. 46** *The calcium and phosphorus are low on the paste test in spite of the good numbers shown on the standard test. Magnesium is low, but about where one might expect it to be, and the potassium is higher than expected. The trace elements are all low with the exception of iron.*

## Low Exchange Capacity Soils Standard Test
## Example 6: Golf Course Greens
## Samples 1 & 2

These two soil samples were sent in from golf course greens. At first glance the samples might appear to be in the wrong section. The samples look like they belong in the high exchange soils section and certainly not this low exchange section. These samples are truly sandy soils, but much of the sand is calcareous sand. This is what soil tests look like when the Mehlich extraction solution dissolves the calcareous sand. Large amounts of calcium end up in the extracting solution and upon the summation of the cations the exchange capacity is blown out of proportion. Consequently, the desired values are dramatically increased causing potassium and magnesium to look extremely deficient (Figure 47). These soils are better suited for a pH-neutral extracting solution like ammonium acetate. Some calcium will still dissolve out into the solution until the pH approaches 8.3, however this is very minimal when ammonium acetate is used.

Personally I think the paste analysis is the best test for these soils since it reflects more of what the plants are seeing. We know that these soils are sands with a very small holding capacity and that we will be applying fertilizer at a little over removal rates, so why run a standard soil test that may give erratic results and was not designed for these types of soils?

Phosphorus is a good example to illustrate this point using the standard test. Sample 1 shows only 40 lbs. phosphorus per acre while Sample 2 shows 249 lbs. per acre (Figure 47). Is Sample 1 really that low? The paste test, which I would be more inclined to depend upon, does not substantiate that value. Why does the phosphorus come through higher on one test and not the other? There could be many factors, but I would look at the calcium and organic matter level in the samples. Sample 2 is about 25% higher in organic matter—

possibly lending to an increased buffering capacity or organic phosphorus sources not impacted by the high calcium content. Sample 2 also has about 46% less calcium in the soil. The point is that calcareous sands extracted using the industry standard methods lend themselves to more extrapolation and interpretation of the data.

The standard test for Sample 1 does indicate a much lower potassium, copper and zinc level than Sample 2. Based on this test alone I would have erroneously applied extra phosphorus to Sample 1 and failed to address the trace element deficiencies of boron and manganese since they were listed as adequate.

## Low Exchange Capacity Soils Standard Test
## Example 6: Golf Course Greens Samples 1 & 2

| | | | Green | Green |
|---|---|---|---|---|
| Sample Location | | | Green | Green |
| Sample ID | | | 1 | 2 |
| Lab Number | | | 89 | 90 |
| Sample Depth (inches) | | | 4 | 4 |
| Total Exchange Capacity (m.e.) | | | 35.65 | 24.73 |
| pH of Soil Sample | | | 7.50 | 7.50 |
| Organic Matter (percent) | | | 1.85 | 2.33 |
| Anions | SULFUR: | p.p.m. | 15 | 36 |
| | Mehlich III Phosphorus: | as ($P_2O_5$) lbs. / acre | 40 | 249 |
| Exchangeable Cations | CALCIUM: lbs. / acre | Desired Value | 6464 | 4483 |
| | | Value Found | 8646 | 5819 |
| | | Deficit | | |
| | MAGNESIUM: lbs. / acre | Desired Value | 684 | 474 |
| | | Value Found | 259 | 252 |
| | | Deficit | -425 | -222 |
| | POTASSIUM: lbs. / acre | Desired Value | 741 | 514 |
| | | Value Found | 71 | 132 |
| | | Deficit | -670 | -382 |
| | SODIUM: | lbs. / acre | 25 | 34 |
| Base Saturation % | Calcium (60 to 70%) | | 90.95 | 88.25 |
| | Magnesium (10 to 20%) | | 4.54 | 6.37 |
| | Potassium (2 to 5%) | | 0.38 | 1.03 |
| | Sodium (0.5 to 3%) | | 0.23 | 0.45 |
| | Other Bases (Variable) | | 3.90 | 3.90 |
| | Exchangeable Hydrogen (10 to 15%) | | 0.00 | 0.00 |
| Trace Elements | Boron (ppm) | | 0.69 | 1.17 |
| | Iron (ppm) | | 102 | 192 |
| | Manganese (ppm) | | 35 | 74 |
| | Copper (ppm) | | 1.1 | 3.18 |
| | Zinc (ppm) | | 2.85 | 9.78 |
| | Aluminum (ppm) | | 36 | 127 |

**Fig. 47** *In these samples much of the sand is calcareous sand. This is what soil tests look like when Mehlich extraction is used and dissolves the calcareous sand making large amounts of calcium end up in the extracting solution, blowing the exchange capacity out of proportion and making the potassium and magnesium look extremely deficient. The paste test (Figure 48) done on these same samples is a more accurate reflection of the nutrient availability.*

## Low Exchange Capacity Soils Paste Test
## Example 6: Golf Course Greens Samples 1 & 2

The phosphorus results from the paste test indicate that an adequate amount of phosphorus is in solution, therefore adding maintenance levels of phosphorus would be a good starting point. The nutrient removal rates for several main agricultural crops are listed in Figure 11. Removal levels of phosphorus and potassium for turfgrass should be based on tissue analysis. In looking at some turfgrass tissue analysis that I have, on average the results indicate that for every 1,000 lbs. of turfgrass clippings taken off, approximately 0.3 lbs. of $P_2O_5$ and 0.6 lbs. of $K_2O$ will be removed. This is equivalent to adding nearly 0.6 lbs.of MAP and 1.2 lbs. of potassium sulfate (0-0-50) to compensate for the nutrient removal.

The calcium and the magnesium do not quite meet the paste guidelines for low exchange capacity soils shown in Figure 16. One would think that the calcium in solution should be much higher since the pH and standard test calcium levels are high. The coarseness of the sand particles and the high pH lowers the solubility of the calcareous sand to less than 5 percent. The result is low calcium and magnesium in solution. For plants, this is similar to the "water, water everywhere but not a drop to drink" scenario that a survivor faces when lost at sea. The plants can be surrounded by calcium or other nutrients, but unless the nutrients are soluble and in the right form, their availability is zero. The calcium levels in this example may still be enough providing growth rates are not accelerated by nitrogen and weather conditions.

The nitrogen of choice would be ammonium sulfate, which is rather acidic and could help dissolve some calcium. Magnesium could be supplemented through the use of ProMag or K-Mag at 25 lbs. or 100 lbs. per acre respectively.

The potassium level is good in Sample 2 requiring only maintenance applications, but Sample 1 needs maintenance amounts plus some extra potassium possibly in the form of potassium sulfate or potassium chloride (depending on availability). Note that irrigation water with high chlorides might prevent the use of potassium chloride.

The trace elements are all low in Sample 1 with the exception of iron. I would not be afraid to foliar feed the copper, manganese, boron and zinc. Broadcasting 5 lbs. per acre of copper sulfate, 15 lbs. per acre of manganese sulfate, 10 lbs. per acre of a 10-12% granular boron, and 20 lbs. per acre of zinc sulfate could be done providing incorporation is possible. It would be good to follow up with a tissue analysis to verify uptake and availability. Sample 2 is a little short on boron and zinc, however a tissue sample should be done prior to receiving any foliar or broadcast applications.

## Low Exchange Capacity Soils Paste Test
## Example 6: Golf Course Greens Samples 1 & 2

| Sample Location | | | Green | Green |
|---|---|---|---|---|
| Sample Id | | | 1 | 2 |
| Lab Number | | | 11283 | 11284 |
| Water Used | | | DI | DI |
| pH | | | 7.5 | 7.5 |
| Soluble Salts | | ppm | 213 | 231 |
| Chloride (Cl) | | ppm | 5 | 5 |
| Bicarbonate (HCO$_3$) | | ppm | 107 | 122 |
| Anions | **SULFUR** | ppm | 1.37 | 14.15 |
| | **PHOSPHORUS** | ppm | 0.46 | 0.39 |
| Soluble Cations | **CALCIUM** | ppm | 23.87 | 27.21 |
| | | meq/l | 1.19 | 1.36 |
| | **MAGNESIUM** | ppm | 4.16 | 4.92 |
| | | meq/l | 0.35 | 0.41 |
| | **POTASSIUM** | ppm | 8.38 | 14.51 |
| | | meq/l | 0.22 | 0.38 |
| | **SODIUM** | ppm | 5.27 | 10.81 |
| | | meq/l | 0.23 | 0.47 |
| Percent | Calcium | | 60.07 | 51.97 |
| | Magnesium | | 17.44 | 15.68 |
| | Potassium | | 10.96 | 14.40 |
| | Sodium | | 11.54 | 17.95 |
| Trace Elements | Boron (ppm) | | 0.03 | 0.04 |
| | Iron (ppm) | | 1.39 | 3.46 |
| | Manganese (ppm) | | 0.03 | 0.08 |
| | Copper (ppm) | | 0.04 | 0.06 |
| | Zinc (ppm) | | < 0.02 | 0.04 |
| | Aluminum (ppm) | | 2.85 | 9.17 |

**Fig. 48** *The phosphorus results from the paste test indicate that an adequate amount of phosphorus is in solution. Using the paste method for this sandy sample will give a more accurate reading of the quantity of the nutrients that the plants are able to use.*

## Low Exchange Capacity Soils Standard and Paste Test Example 7: Chicken Layer Manured Field Sample WM-1A-N

Upon examining the results, based on the high exchange capacity, this soil sample appears to be in the wrong section. This is a very sandy soil however due to the high rates of chicken manure applied over the years, the excess calcium picked up in the extraction process masks the real exchange capacity which is around 7 m.e. This field was run initially as a paste test because the fertilizer company had already done a standard test on it and said they could not see any problem with it. The field was yielding poorly, though, and struggling to get a good stand. The initial paste test showed the calcium and magnesium levels to be low. Therefore 1,000 lbs. per acre of gypsum, which contained 3% magnesium, was applied and the following year the crop responded very well. The next year I picked this farmer up as a client and began a testing program. In 2005 the soil still showed some residual effect of the gypsum. Our supply of gypsum with the 3% magnesium dried up and 150 lbs. of K-Mag was applied to boost the low magnesium level. As you can see in the 2006 paste test the magnesium continued to fall (Figure 50). The K-Mag was boosted to 250 lbs. per acre. The crops are doing well, but the K-Mag is getting hard to get. Two thousand pounds per acre of dolomite lime will be applied in the future to supply the magnesium. In spite of the high pH, the phosphorus is still high enough in solubility so even if the dolomite lime cuts the soluble phosphorus in half, the level will still be very good. Since the soil pH is 7.1, I expect the solubility of the lime to be around 5% which would release approximately the equivalent of 100 lbs. of K-Mag per acre. Following up next year with both the standard and paste test will help determine the validity of this recommendation. This example is why I wrote this book. Sometimes you must think outside the box and try something unconventional. The testing tools are there to verify the successes and failures.

# Low Exchange Capacity Soils Standard Test
# Example 7: Chicken Layer Manured Field
# Sample WM-1A-N

| | | WM-1A-N | WM-1A-N |
|---|---|---|---|
| Sample Location | | WM-1A-N | WM-1A-N |
| Sample Id (Year) | | 2005 | 2006 |
| Lab Number | | 6 | 97 |
| Sample Depth (inches) | | | |
| Total Exchange Capacity (m.e.) | | 15.97 | 12.81 |
| pH of Soil Sample | | 7.00 | 7.10 |
| Organic Matter (percent) | | 2.26 | 1.78 |
| **Anions** SULFUR: p.p.m. | | 17 | 9 |
| Mehlich III Phosphorus: as (P$_2$O$_5$) lbs./acre | | 3132 | 4138 |
| **Exchangeable Cations** CALCIUM: lbs./acre Value Found | | 5398 | 4241 |
| MAGNESIUM: lbs./acre Value Found | | 269 | 181 |
| POTASSIUM: lbs./acre Value Found Deficit | | 422 | 594 |
| SODIUM: lbs./acre | | 50 | 64 |
| **Base Saturation %** Calcium (60 to 70%) | | 84.51 | 82.79 |
| Magnesium (10 to 20%) | | 7.02 | 5.89 |
| Potassium (2 to 5%) | | 3.39 | 5.94 |
| Sodium (0.5 to 3%) | | 0.68 | 1.08 |
| Other Bases (Variable) | | 4.40 | 4.30 |
| Exchangeable Hydrogen (10 to 15%) | | 0.00 | 0.00 |
| **Trace Elements** Boron (ppm) | | 0.62 | 0.27 |
| Iron (ppm) | | 253 | 183 |
| Manganese (ppm) | | 140 | 39 |
| Copper (ppm) | | 5.04 | 2.81 |
| Zinc (ppm) | | 12.75 | 7.84 |
| Aluminum (ppm) | | 588 | 459 |

**Fig. 49** *This is a very sandy soil, however due to the high rates of chicken manure having been applied over the years, the excess calcium picked up in the extraction process masks the real exchange capacity which is around 7 m.e.*

## Low Exchange Capacity Soils Paste Test Example 7: Chicken Layer Manured Field Sample WM-1A-N

| Sample Location | WM-1A-N | WM-1A-N | WM-1A-N |
|---|---|---|---|
| Sample Name | 2003 | 2005 | 2006 |
| Lab Number | 812 | 1931 | 6121 |
| | | | |
| pH | 7.3 | 7.0 | 7.1 |
| | | | |
| Phosphorus | 1.4 | 1.4 | 1.9 |
| Calcium | 10.7 | 18.1 | 17.1 |
| Magnesium | 1.2 | 2.3 | 1.6 |
| Potassium | 13.0 | 10.1 | 14.4 |
| Sodium | 1.3 | 3.8 | 0.9 |
| Sulfur | 0.2 | 1.1 | 0.6 |
| | | | |
| Boron | 0.06 | 0.03 | 0.02 |
| Iron | 1.76 | 6.33 | 1.25 |
| Manganese | 0.09 | 0.29 | 0.04 |
| Copper | 0.06 | <0.02 | < 0.02 |
| Zinc | 0.03 | 0.03 | < 0.02 |
| Aluminum | 1.86 | 7.04 | 1.25 |
| Molybdenum | 0.01 | 0.07 | 0.01 |
| Cobalt | 0.01 | < 0.01 | < 0.01 |
| | | | |
| Calcium % | 52.0 | 59.6 | 50.3 |
| Magnesium % | 9.8 | 12.4 | 4.8 |
| Potassium % | 32.5 | 17.1 | 42.4 |
| Sodium % | 5.7 | 10.9 | 2.6 |
| | | | |
| Calcium %:Magnesium % | 5.3 | 4.8 | 10.5 |

**Fig. 50** *In spite of the high pH the phosphorus is still adequately high in solubility. As you can see in the 2006 paste test results in the right column that the magnesium continued to fall. Since the soil pH is 7.1, I expect the solubility of the lime to be around 5%, which would release approximately the equivalent of 100 lbs. of K-Mag per acre.*

## Low Exchange Capacity Soils Standard and Paste Test Example 8: Indiana Golf Course Green Samples 12 & 17

These samples were collected from an Indiana golf course green; first a note about this sample and the testing instructions. The individual who collected these samples knew that the golf greens were being top dressed with calcareous sand and decided to ask the lab to run the samples with an ammonium acetate extraction solution. The ammonium acetate extracting solution has a pH of 7, so it is less likely to dissolve sand grains and elevate the exchange capacity and the desired values. The calcium and magnesium numbers certainly look reasonable, but may almost be too low for the pH and the base saturation balance.

This brings us to the second thing that should be noticed at the top of the soil report—the depth of sample. This sample was collected at 3 inches; therefore the desired values and reported values will be cut in half compared to the typical 6-inch samples. This goes back to the assumption that a 3-inch depth sample over an acre weighs about 1 million pounds and a 6-inch sample will weigh approximately 2 million pounds. Consequently the nutrient values collected from the ICP in parts per million are multiplied by 1 at the 3 inch depth and multiplied by 2 at the 6 inch depth. Most of our desired levels are based on a 6-inch depth of sampling.

These samples based on the standard test are about as good as it gets. The potassium results on Sample 12 could be improved, but that is about all there is of note.

The solubility threshold numbers are pretty much in agreement with the standard test, however the solution balance is a little off. I would not really feel the need to elevate the calcium levels just to bring the percent of calcium and magnesium closer to 3 to 1 ratio. The higher magnesium levels don't impact soil physics nearly as much in sands as it does in the heavier soils.

The bicarbonate levels are high, probably due to the irrigation water (Figure 53). As these soils dry the bicarbonates can react with the free calcium in solution and precipitate it out. At the same time the calcium carbonate can react with anions such as phosphates and borates and precipitate them out of solution. It is similar to the domino effect. Flushing the soils when irrigating or neutralizing the bicarbonates with acid before irrigating will help to reduce the buildup of this anion.

The following table (Figure 51) taken from the Brookside Laboratories training manual shows the amount of 95% sulfuric acid needed to neutralize 90% of the bicarbonates in an acre-foot of water.

### Sulfuric Acid Required to Neutralize Bicarbonates

| Bicarbonate (ppm) | Acid Required | | |
|---|---|---|---|
| | (ppm) | Lbs. | Gallons |
| 50 | 38 | 103 | 7 |
| 100 | 76 | 206 | 13 |
| 200 | 152 | 412 | 27 |
| 400 | 304 | 824 | 55 |

*Table data courtesy of Brookside Laboratories.*

**Fig. 51** *Quantities of 95% sulfuric acid required to neutralize 90% of bicarbonates in an acre-foot of water.*

The paste test (Figure 53) shows that the boron is below the detection limit (<0.02), but is quite adequate on the standard test (Figure 52). Based on this scenario I would depend on a foliar program rather than a soil broadcast application. A tissue analysis would also help determine if any other trace element was not being picked up in adequate amounts.

If this analysis were for general agriculture crops such as corn, beans or wheat, I would not do a lot differently from the turfgrass recommendations except to elevate the potassium levels. On the low exchange capacity soils there is not enough room to hold all the necessary nutrients for a 200-bushel corn crop unless we can establish a root system much deeper than six inches. It is for this reason that I would incorporate into my starters products like ACA, Asset or humic acids, which are root stimulators, in order to promote a vigorous and deep root system.

Multiple nitrogen applications or multiple nitrogen sources that incorporate slow release technology would be a given on these light exchange capacity soils whether you're growing turfgrass, vegetables or corn. Incorporating in high-end molecular weight humic acid products with UAN solutions provide exchange sites to hold both the positive and negative ions. These humic acids are also very beneficial for phosphorus as well.

# Low Exchange Capacity Soils Standard Test
## Example 8: Indiana Golf Course Green Samples 12 & 17

| Sample Location | | | Green 12 | Green 17 |
|---|---|---|---|---|
| | | | | |
| Lab Number | | | 25 | 26 |
| Sample Depth (inches) | | | 3 | 3 |
| Total Exchange Capacity (m.e.) | | | 6.33 | 6.68 |
| pH of Soil Sample | | | 6.70 | 6.70 |
| Organic Matter (percent) | | | 2.28 | 2.23 |
| Anions | SULFUR: | p.p.m. | 9 | 9 |
| | Mehlich III Phosphorus: | as ($P_2O_5$) lbs. / acre | 321 | 229 |
| Exchangeable Cations | CALCIUM: lbs. / acre | Desired Value | 860 | 908 |
| | | Value Found | 884 | 856 |
| | | Deficit | | -52 |
| | MAGNESIUM: lbs. / acre | Desired Value | 100 | 100 |
| | | Value Found | 122 | 133 |
| | | Deficit | | |
| | POTASSIUM: lbs. / acre | Desired Value | 100 | 104 |
| | | Value Found | 53 | 188 |
| | | Deficit | -47 | |
| | SODIUM: | lbs. / acre | 40 | 45 |
| Base Saturation % | Calcium (60 to 70%) | | 69.87 | 64.08 |
| | Magnesium (10 to 20%) | | 16.07 | 16.59 |
| | Potassium (2 to 5%) | | 2.15 | 7.22 |
| | Sodium (0.5 to 3%) | | 2.78 | 2.92 |
| | Other Bases (Variable) | | 4.70 | 4.70 |
| | Exchangeable Hydrogen (10 to 15%) | | 4.50 | 4.50 |
| Trace Elements | Boron (ppm) | | 0.69 | 0.6 |
| | Iron (ppm) | | 321 | 239 |
| | Manganese (ppm) | | 61 | 74 |
| | Copper (ppm) | | 2 | 2.11 |
| | Zinc (ppm) | | 6.95 | 6.73 |
| | Aluminum (ppm) | | 133 | 172 |

**Fig. 52** *The calcium and magnesium numbers certainly look reasonable in this standard test, but may almost be too low for the pH and the base saturation balance. This sample was collected at 3 inches in depth, therefore the desired values and reported values are cut in half compared to the typical 6-inch samples.*

## Low Exchange Capacity Soils Paste Test
## Example 8: Indiana Golf Course Green Samples 12 & 17

| Sample Location | | | Green 12 | Green 17 |
|---|---|---|---|---|
| Lab Number | | | 14456 | 14457 |
| Water Used | | | DI | DI |
| pH | | | 6.7 | 6.7 |
| Soluble Salts | | ppm | 202 | 189 |
| Chloride (Cl) | | ppm | 11 | 10 |
| Bicarbonate (HCO$_3$) | | ppm | 222 | 188 |
| Anions | SULFUR | ppm | 8.85 | 7.35 |
| | PHOSPHORUS | ppm | 2.56 | 0.52 |
| Soluble Cations | CALCIUM | ppm | 35.95 | 34.99 |
| | | meq/l | 1.80 | 1.75 |
| | MAGNESIUM | ppm | 13.1 | 12.37 |
| | | meq/l | 1.09 | 1.03 |
| | POTASSIUM | ppm | 14.89 | 11.46 |
| | | meq/l | 0.39 | 0.30 |
| | SODIUM | ppm | 7.86 | 6.31 |
| | | meq/l | 0.34 | 0.27 |
| Percent | Calcium | | 49.68 | 52.19 |
| | Magnesium | | 30.17 | 30.75 |
| | Potassium | | 10.69 | 8.88 |
| | Sodium | | 9.45 | 8.18 |
| Trace Elements | Boron (ppm) | | < 0.02 | < 0.02 |
| | Iron (ppm) | | 1 | 0.55 |
| | Manganese (ppm) | | 0.32 | 0.53 |
| | Copper (ppm) | | 0.05 | 0.06 |
| | Zinc (ppm) | | 0.04 | 0.05 |
| | Aluminum (ppm) | | 1.4 | 0.83 |

**Fig. 53** *The paste test shows that boron is below the detection limit (<0.02), but is quite adequate on the standard test. Based on this depend on a foliar program rather than a soil broadcast application.*

## Low Exchange Capacity Soils Standard and Paste Test Example 9: Finland Garden Samples 2 and 7

These samples were collected from a garden in Finland. The soils fall into the low exchange capacity section and were sampled six inches deep. The standard test for Samples 2 and 7 looks fairly good for the major elements. A little increase in potassium on both samples and some high calcium lime on Sample 7 would appear to fix most of the major elements. Boron, manganese, copper and zinc are low in the standard test. Broadcasting 15 lbs. of 10% boron, 10-20 lbs. of manganese sulfate, 5 lbs. of copper sulfate and 15-20 lbs. of zinc sulfate per acre on the soil would be a start for a trace element program based on the standard test. Divide the above-mentioned recommendation amounts by 43 to come up with the pounds needed per 1,000 ft$^2$.

The pH is ideal for trace element solubility, but with organic matter around 2.5% trace elements along with water-holding capacity will be low. Since this is a garden sample the organic matter level could be increased with large amounts of organic wastes, compost or organic residues such as leaves or straw. These organic materials will not only increase the organic matter but also the mineral content in the soil. Building up the organic matter would preclude any addition of nutrients to the soil until the organic matter had a season to degrade and reach equilibrium in the soil. Adding organic matter already composted would greatly speed this process up. If organic material is added to the soil with a carbon nitrogen ratio greater than 30:1, then extra nitrogen will need to be added in order to keep the microbes from robbing your plants of nitrogen as they break down the residue. Using straw as mulch during the growing season is a great way to reduce weed pressure and moisture loss on a low organic matter, light exchange capacity soil. When the season is over, incorporate the straw along with 2-3 lbs. of nitrogen per 1,000 ft$^2$ to speed the decomposition before the next season.

The paste test lines up very well with our trace element conclusions that we made based on the standard test. The trace element values on the paste test are low enough that I would also include some foliar trace elements applications during the growing season.

The major elements on the paste test are quite different than the standard test data. The paste analysis would require me to change my thoughts on what I might do with the calcium and magnesium. The calcium and magnesium threshold numbers are very low, therefore I would use 6 lbs. per 1,000 ft² or 240 lbs. per acre of K-Mag on Sample 2 along with 25 lbs. per 1,000 ft² or 1,000 lbs. per acre of gypsum. Since the pH is 6 on Sample 7, I would use 2,000 pounds of a fine dolomite lime or 50 lbs. per 1,000 ft² along with 25 lbs. per 1,000 ft² or 1,000 lbs. per acre of gypsum. The pH would increase as a result of the dolomite lime. The calcium and magnesium solubility levels would also increase and the addition of gypsum would help to widen the ratio of soluble calcium to magnesium. The lime and gypsum should be thoroughly incorporated into the soil.

Because of all the soluble calcium and magnesium being applied to the soil, I might temporarily tie up some phosphorus. This would not be as big an issue if the calcium products were applied in the fall, but if they were applied in the spring prior to planting I would apply some phosphorus to help offset any tie up and increase the solubility.

Equal amounts of potassium could be added to both samples providing compost or some organic product was not applied. I would start off with 4-5 lbs. per 1,000 ft² or 150-200 lbs. per acre of potassium chloride or potassium sulfate in the fall preferably incorporated with the lime and gypsum. Another 2-3 lbs. per 1,000 ft² could be applied in the spring prior to planting.

## Low Exchange Capacity Soils Standard Test
## Example 9: Finland Garden Samples 2 & 7

| | | | Garden 2 | Garden 7 |
|---|---|---|---|---|
| Sample Location | | | Garden 2 | Garden 7 |
| Sample ID | | | | |
| Lab Number | | | 33 | 34 |
| Sample Depth (inches) | | | 6 | 6 |
| Total Exchange Capacity (m.e.) | | | 8.12 | 7.36 |
| pH of Soil Sample | | | 6.50 | 6.00 |
| Organic Matter (percent) | | | 2.58 | 2.26 |
| Anions | SULFUR: | p.p.m. | 16 | 15 |
| | Mehlich III Phosphorus: | as ($P_2O_5$) lbs. / acre | 705 | 554 |
| Exchangeable Cations | CALCIUM: lbs. / acre | Desired Value | 2208 | 2001 |
| | | Value Found | 2234 | 1737 |
| | | Deficit | | -264 |
| | MAGNESIUM: lbs. / acre | Desired Value | 233 | 211 |
| | | Value Found | 287 | 286 |
| | | Deficit | | |
| | POTASSIUM: lbs. / acre | Desired Value | 253 | 229 |
| | | Value Found | 212 | 197 |
| | | Deficit | -41 | -32 |
| | SODIUM: | lbs. / acre | 28 | 32 |
| Base Saturation % | Calcium (60 to 70%) | | 68.79 | 59.02 |
| | Magnesium (10 to 20%) | | 14.73 | 16.19 |
| | Potassium (2 to 5%) | | 3.35 | 3.43 |
| | Sodium (0.5 to 3%) | | 0.76 | 0.95 |
| | Other Bases (Variable) | | 4.90 | 5.40 |
| | Exchangeable Hydrogen (10 to 15%) | | 7.50 | 15.00 |
| Trace Elements | Boron (ppm) | | 0.48 | 0.49 |
| | Iron (ppm) | | 464 | 427 |
| | Manganese (ppm) | | 14 | 14 |
| | Copper (ppm) | | 1.46 | 1.92 |
| | Zinc (ppm) | | 3.09 | 2.63 |
| | Aluminum (ppm) | | 350 | 337 |

**Fig. 54** *The standard test for Samples 2 and 7 looks fairly good for the major elements. Boron, manganese, copper and zinc are low in the standard test. The pH is ideal for trace element solubility, but with organic matter around 2.5 percent, trace elements along with water-holding capacity will be low.*

## Low Exchange Capacity Soils Paste Test
## Example 9: Finland Garden Samples 2 & 7

| Sample Location | | | Garden 2 | Garden 7 |
|---|---|---|---|---|
| Sample Id | | | | |
| Lab Number | | | 12300 | 12301 |
| Water Used | | | DI | DI |
| pH | | | 6.5 | 6 |
| Soluble Salts | | ppm | 122 | 106 |
| Chloride (Cl) | | ppm | 11 | 11 |
| Bicarbonate (HCO$_3$) | | ppm | 46 | 34 |
| Anions | SULFUR | ppm | 5.88 | 7.94 |
| | PHOSPHORUS | ppm | 0.14 | 0.28 |
| Soluble Cations | CALCIUM | ppm | 7.82 | 4.88 |
| | | meq/l | 0.39 | 0.24 |
| | MAGNESIUM | ppm | 1.82 | 1.57 |
| | | meq/l | 0.15 | 0.13 |
| | POTASSIUM | ppm | 8.66 | 7.7 |
| | | meq/l | 0.22 | 0.20 |
| | SODIUM | ppm | 3.57 | 5.51 |
| | | meq/l | 0.16 | 0.24 |
| Percent | Calcium | | 42.39 | 29.97 |
| | Magnesium | | 16.42 | 16.03 |
| | Potassium | | 24.39 | 24.55 |
| | Sodium | | 16.81 | 29.45 |
| Trace Elements | Boron (ppm) | | < 0.02 | < 0.02 |
| | Iron (ppm) | | 1.09 | 1.48 |
| | Manganese (ppm) | | 0.03 | 0.05 |
| | Copper (ppm) | | 0.02 | 0.04 |
| | Zinc (ppm) | | < 0.02 | < 0.02 |
| | Aluminum (ppm) | | 1.89 | 2.84 |

**Fig. 55** *The trace element values on the paste test are low enough that I would include some foliar trace elements applications during the growing season. The major elements on the paste test are quite different than the standard test data. The calcium and magnesium threshold numbers are very low.*

*Chapter 6*

# Investigating High Exchange Capacity Soils

## High Exchange Capacity Soils Standard and Paste Tests Example 1: Texas Sample A

These samples are calcareous soils collected in Texas. Three different extractions for the various cations were preformed on the same soil sample A; Mehlich III (the industry standard), paste analysis, and ammonium acetate extraction. Keep in mind that the ammonium acetate extracting solutions are just for the cations. The rest of the test—minors, phosphorus and sulfur—are the results from the Mehlich III extraction. The paste extraction was performed with distilled water (Figure 57).

This soil has an exchange capacity greater than 10 so we will be balancing the soil based on the BCSR method. The pH is very high and the probability of getting the pH down to 6.2 is not very realistic. This sample is calcareous by nature; however it is possible to have carbonates and other salts move up into the surface profile during extended periods of dry weather, dramatically affecting the soil test results and nutrient availability.

The calcium and magnesium values are excessively high from the Mehlich test resulting in an exaggerated exchange capacity and unrealistic desired values. Therefore, to balance this soil, the ammonium acetate extraction is used to determine the desired values. Keep in mind that even the ammonium acetate numbers could also be overstated. K-Mag at 200-250 lbs. per acre would not supply all the magnesium needed to correct the deficiency in the soil, but would be a start in the right direction.

I would not necessarily try to correct the magnesium deficiency on the Mehlich or ammonium acetate soil tests. Turning to the paste analysis I could balance the solution by getting 6-8 ppm of magnesium in solution. The 200 lbs. per acre of K-Mag (with 11% magnesium) would supply approximately 11 ppm of magnesium (assuming 100% solubility of the product). Dispersion, root growth, tie-ups and nutrient interferences would ultimately determine whether the crop could pick up the appropriate nutrients and in the proper amounts. This is where following up with tissue analysis would help verify your course of action. Although there is already a good level of potassium in this soil, I feel extra potassium would be needed to push the paste test to the 12-15 ppm desired level and help cover the removal rates. If the flow rates of potassium from the soil colloid were high enough, the potassium rates might be reduced. Always cover the removal rates of all the nutrients with a fertilizer application either post-season or pre-season for the next crop unless you are trying to pull down previous excess applications.

The phosphorus levels are very low in all three tests and will more than likely remain low until the free calcium carbonates are lowered and the pH drops below 6.8. An Olsen phosphorus test is oftentimes used in these situations with high pH, however I personally would rather spend my testing dollars on a paste and tissue test for determining phosphorus availability. Leaching the calcium out with rainwater would be an immense help, but in arid and semi-arid soils the odds are good that it will not change much and you must accept the situation and use band and/or foliar methods to apply phosphorus fertilizers. In this situation I would add at least the phosphorus removal rates in a band application. Adding nitrogen and possibly something like a humic acid could help maintain phosphorus availability.

Boron and manganese appear to be fairly high in the Mehlich III extractions, while iron and zinc are quite low. The paste test is quite different. The boron, copper and zinc are all below the detection level (<0.02 ppm), but iron and manganese are quite adequate in the paste test. Before making a blanket application of traces on any crop it would be advisable to run a tissue test and verify the shortages.

Even manganese, which is fairly good in solution and very high in the standard test, could become short if the soils were loose and airy and if glyphosate has been applied. At the risk of becoming redundant, tissue test to avoid the chance of wasting money and potential toxicities. In the next example, which is similar to this one, we will explore the possibility of broadcasting traces to adjust the low levels identified on the soil tests.

# High Exchange Capacity Soils Standard Tests using Mehlich III vs. Ammonium Acetate extraction. Example 1: Texas Sample A

| Sample Location | | | Ammonium | Mehlich III |
|---|---|---|---|---|
| Sample ID | | | Acetate A | A |
| Lab Number | | | 162 | 22 |
| Sample Depth (inches) | | | 6 | 6 |
| Total Exchange Capacity (m.e.) | | | 31.07 | 40.87 |
| pH of Soil Sample | | | 7.80 | 7.80 |
| Organic Matter (percent) | | | 2.77 | 2.77 |
| Anions | SULFUR: | p.p.m. | 56 | 56 |
| | Mehlich III Phosphorus: | as ($P_2O_5$) lbs. / acre | 48 | 48 |
| Exchangeable Cations | CALCIUM: lbs. / acre | Desired Value | 8449 | 11117 |
| | | Value Found | 10935 | 14487 |
| | | Deficit | | |
| | MAGNESIUM: lbs. / acre | Desired Value | 894 | 1177 |
| | | Value Found | 362 | 482 |
| | | Deficit | -532 | -695 |
| | POTASSIUM: lbs. / acre | Desired Value | 969 | 1275 |
| | | Value Found | 800 | 861 |
| | | Deficit | -169 | -414 |
| | SODIUM: | lbs. / acre | 35 | 34 |
| Base Saturation % | Calcium (60 to 70%) | | 88.00 | 88.61 |
| | Magnesium (10 to 20%) | | 4.86 | 4.91 |
| | Potassium (2 to 5%) | | 3.30 | 2.70 |
| | Sodium (0.5 to 3%) | | 0.25 | 0.18 |
| | Other Bases (Variable) | | 3.60 | 3.60 |
| | Exchangeable Hydrogen (10 to 15%) | | 0.00 | 0.00 |
| Trace Elements | Boron (ppm) | | 1.15 | 1.15 |
| | Iron (ppm) | | 29 | 29 |
| | Manganese (ppm) | | 212 | 212 |
| | Copper (ppm) | | 2.46 | 2.46 |
| | Zinc (ppm) | | 3.8 | 3.8 |
| | Aluminum (ppm) | | 587 | 587 |

**Fig. 56** *The pH is very high and the probability of getting the pH down to 6.2 is not very realistic. The calcium and magnesium values are excessively high from the Mehlich III test resulting in an exaggerated exchange capacity and unrealistic desired values. Boron, copper and zinc are all below the detection level, but iron and manganese are quite adequate in the paste test.*

# High Exchange Capacity Soils Paste Test
## Example 1: Texas Sample A

| Sample Location | | | A |
|---|---|---|---|
| | | | |
| Lab Number | | | 13945 |
| Water Used | | | DI |
| pH | | | 7.8 |
| Soluble Salts | | ppm | 129 |
| Chloride (Cl) | | ppm | 5 |
| Bicarbonate (HCO$_3$) | | ppm | 105 |
| Anions | SULFUR | ppm | 7.78 |
| | PHOSPHORUS | ppm | < 0.1 |
| Soluble Cations | CALCIUM | ppm | 35.09 |
| | | meq/l | 1.75 |
| | MAGNESIUM | ppm | 1.73 |
| | | meq/l | 0.14 |
| | POTASSIUM | ppm | 4.32 |
| | | meq/l | 0.11 |
| | SODIUM | ppm | 2.8 |
| | | meq/l | 0.12 |
| Percent | Calcium | | 82.28 |
| | Magnesium | | 6.76 |
| | Potassium | | 5.26 |
| | Sodium | | 5.71 |
| Trace Elements | Boron (ppm) | | < 0.02 |
| | Iron (ppm) | | 1.23 |
| | Manganese (ppm) | | 0.06 |
| | Copper (ppm) | | < 0.02 |
| | Zinc (ppm) | | < 0.02 |
| | Aluminum (ppm) | | 3.04 |

**Fig. 57** *Although there is already a good level of potassium in this soil, extra potassium would be needed to push the paste test to the 12-15 ppm desired level and help cover the removal rates.*

## High Exchange Capacity Soils Standard and Paste Test Example 2: Texas Samples East and West

These two samples also came from a high calcareous area in Texas. Three different extractions for the various cations were preformed on the two soil samples; Mehlich III (the industry standard), paste analysis and ammonium acetate. These samples are similar to Example 1, but here the TEC drops almost in half when running the ammonium acetate extraction and comparing it to the Mehlich extraction. The calcium and magnesium base saturation balance does not change dramatically, but the numbers look more realistic. Potassium is the least affected by the two extracting solutions (Mehlich III and Ammonium Acetate) since much of the potassium is not tied to carbonate compounds. The high level of potassium can exacerbate the low magnesium level through interference issues. K-Mag might not help as much in this example since it would continue to add to an already high potassium level.

Magnesium sulfate or magnesium oxysulfate would be a better choice to balance this soil. Supplying enough magnesium to cover the crop demand as well as the 14-15 lbs. of magnesium needed to balance the paste test should be our starting point, adjusting from there after a tissue test.

Like the previous example, the trace elements boron and manganese are high in the Mehlich extractions while zinc, copper and iron appear to be fairly low. Boron, copper and zinc all are at or below the detection limit, while iron and manganese are fairly adequate. Land application of the traces would not be my first choice to correct the trace element issues. Although a case could be made that if all that we do is foliar feed the soils never would get better and the flow rate of traces would  always remain low. It is my feeling that the soils here are so calcareous that applications of traces would tie up as fast as they were applied. One could certainly be justified in questioning the value of the traces on the Mehlich III extractions since the high calcareous nature of these soils have such an impact on the extraction process. I believe foliar feeding  would be the most effective method of raising the levels in the plants providing a tissue test justifies an application.

# High Exchange Capacity Soils Standard Test With Two Different Extractions
## Example 2: Texas Samples East and West

| Sample Location | | Ammonium | Ammonium | Mehlich III | Mehlich III |
|---|---|---|---|---|---|
| Sample ID | | Acetate East | Acetate West | East | West |
| Lab Number | | 160 | 161 | 20 | 21 |
| Sample Depth (inches) | | 6 | 6 | 6 | 6 |
| Total Exchange Capacity (m.e.) | | 24.83 | 23.95 | 42.06 | 40.06 |
| pH of Soil Sample | | 7.90 | 7.90 | 7.90 | 7.90 |
| Organic Matter (percent) | | 2.31 | 1.95 | 2.31 | 1.95 |
| **Anions** SULFUR: p.p.m. | | 31 | 35 | 31 | 35 |
| Mehlich III Phosphorus: as ($P_2O_5$) lbs./acre | | 134 | 91 | 134 | 91 |
| **Exchangeable Cations** CALCIUM: lbs./acre | Desired Value | 6752 | 6513 | 11440 | 10896 |
| | Value Found | 8298 | 7679 | 14618 | 13502 |
| | Deficit | | | | |
| MAGNESIUM: lbs./acre | Desired Value | 714 | 689 | 1211 | 1153 |
| | Value Found | 389 | 470 | 561 | 659 |
| | Deficit | -325 | -219 | -650 | -494 |
| POTASSIUM: lbs./acre | Desired Value | 774 | 747 | 1312 | 1249 |
| | Value Found | 1119 | 1451 | 1239 | 1596 |
| | Deficit | | | -73 | |
| SODIUM: lbs./acre | | 71 | 43 | 55 | 52 |
| **Base Saturation %** Calcium (60 to 70%) | | 83.56 | 80.17 | 86.88 | 84.26 |
| Magnesium (10 to 20%) | | 6.53 | 8.18 | 5.56 | 6.85 |
| Potassium (2 to 5%) | | 5.78 | 7.77 | 3.78 | 5.11 |
| Sodium (0.5 to 3%) | | 0.62 | 0.39 | 0.28 | 0.28 |
| Other Bases (Variable) | | 3.50 | 3.50 | 3.50 | 3.50 |
| Exchangeable Hydrogen (10 to 15%) | | 0.00 | 0.00 | 0.00 | 0.00 |
| **Trace Elements** Boron (ppm) | | 1.32 | 1.33 | 1.32 | 1.33 |
| Iron (ppm) | | 22 | 11 | 22 | 11 |
| Manganese (ppm) | | 140 | 150 | 140 | 150 |
| Copper (ppm) | | 1.82 | 1.74 | 1.82 | 1.74 |
| Zinc (ppm) | | 1.6 | 1.1 | 1.6 | 1.1 |
| Aluminum (ppm) | | 246 | 200 | 246 | 200 |

**Fig. 58** *Potassium is the least affected by the two extracting solutions used here since much of the potassium is not tied to carbonate compounds. The high level of potassium can exacerbate the low magnesium level through interference issues. The trace elements boron and manganese are high in the Mehlich extractions while zinc, copper and iron appear to be fairly low.*

# High Exchange Capacity Soils Paste Test
# Example 2: Texas Samples East and West

| Sample Location | | | East | West |
|---|---|---|---|---|
| Sample Id | | | | |
| Lab Number | | | 13943 | 13944 |
| Water Used | | | DI | DI |
| pH | | | 7.9 | 7.9 |
| Soluble Salts | | ppm | 161 | 180 |
| Chloride (Cl) | | ppm | 7 | 10 |
| Bicarbonate (HCO$_3$) | | ppm | 154 | 134 |
| Anions | SULFUR | ppm | 5.54 | 4 |
| | PHOSPHORUS | ppm | < 0.1 | < 0.1 |
| Soluble Cations | CALCIUM | ppm | 46.04 | 41.19 |
| | | meq/l | 2.30 | 2.06 |
| | MAGNESIUM | ppm | 3.26 | 3.38 |
| | | meq/l | 0.27 | 0.28 |
| | POTASSIUM | ppm | 11.87 | 18.91 |
| | | meq/l | 0.31 | 0.49 |
| | SODIUM | ppm | 8.03 | 6.04 |
| | | meq/l | 0.35 | 0.26 |
| Percent | Calcium | | 71.25 | 66.55 |
| | Magnesium | | 8.40 | 9.10 |
| | Potassium | | 9.54 | 15.87 |
| | Sodium | | 10.81 | 8.49 |
| Trace Elements | Boron (ppm) | | 0.02 | 0.02 |
| | Iron (ppm) | | 0.98 | 1.03 |
| | Manganese (ppm) | | 0.05 | 0.05 |
| | Copper (ppm) | | < 0.02 | < 0.02 |
| | Zinc (ppm) | | < 0.02 | < 0.02 |
| | Aluminum (ppm) | | 2.44 | 2.76 |

**Fig. 59** *Supplying enough magnesium to cover the crop demand as well as the 14-15 pounds of magnesium needed to balance the paste test should be our starting point, adjusting from there after a tissue test. Three traces zinc, copper and boron are all at or near the minimum level of detection using paste testing instruments.*

## High Exchange Capacity Soils Standard and Paste Test Example 3: Porter Landscaping Samples Entire and Laurel

The Porter samples come from a landscaping business in the eastern part of the United States. The samples are identified as "Entire" and "Laurel." Both samples had a standard and paste test performed on them. At first glance the samples fall into the high exchange category and each have high phosphorus and potassium levels. The Laurel sample has a pH about a half a point below our ideal. The sulfur is quite high in this sample, which could represent a drainage issue or an application of a sulfur-bearing fertilizer. If it is a drainage issue, then it must be addressed, but this is outside the scope of this discussion.

The desired levels on these reports are based on 68% calcium, 12% magnesium, and a 4% potassium base saturation standard. My first thought might be to lime the Laurel sample, however looking at the paste test I could certainly forego that idea since the calcium and magnesium levels meet the threshold guidelines and the 5:1 Ca:Mg ratio.

The percentage of calcium and magnesium in the Laurel sample paste test (Figure 61) is low on a percentage basis, but that is due to the high amount of potassium in solution. The Entire sample is really not as well balance in solution as one might think when looking at the standard report (Figure 60). The calcium to magnesium ratio in the solution is 10:1, and the magnesium does not meet the threshold amount of 4-8 ppm. In order to balance the solution in the Entire sample, the magnesium should be approximately 7 ppm to meet the 5:1 ratio and bring the percentage numbers close to the 60% calcium and 20% magnesium. It is also important to notice how much higher the trace elements are in the Laurel sample compared to the Entire sample. The manganese is getting a little high in the Laurel paste test (Figure 61) when it comes to turf and general crops. It is for that reason alone that I would lime with 1,500-2,000 lbs. of dolomite lime per acre. Since the paste test phosphorus came in below the detection limit I would still attempt to apply half to three quarter of the phosphorus removal unless the price of phosphorus is abnormally high at application time. Depending upon the crop, I would foliar feed the boron and copper on the Laurel sample and boron, copper and zinc on the Entire sample. This should be done based on a tissue sample. If the decision is made to go ahead and foliar feed, try to apply the nutrients prior to critical need times. For example, corn should be done pre-6 leaf collar stage and possibly again before ear leaf. I would spray soybeans just prior to and during the first part of flowering. Plants being grown for aesthetics such as turfgrass and foliage could be sprayed at various other intervals during the growing season.

# High Exchange Capacity Soils Standard Test Example 3: Porter Landscaping Samples Entire and Laurel

| Sample Location | | | Porter | Porter |
|---|---|---|---|---|
| Sample ID | | | Laurel | Entire |
| Lab Number | | | 19 | 21 |
| Sample Depth (inches) | | | 6 | 6 |
| Total Exchange Capacity (m.e.) | | | 17.22 | 12.29 |
| pH of Soil Sample | | | 5.80 | 6.50 |
| Organic Matter (percent) | | | 10.22 | 6.71 |
| Anions | SULFUR: | p.p.m. | 112 | 14 |
| | Mehlich III Phosphorus: | as ($P_2O_5$) lbs. / acre | 527 | 389 |
| Exchangeable Cations | CALCIUM: lbs. / acre | Desired Value | 4683 | 3342 |
| | | Value Found | 3984 | 3472 |
| | | Deficit | -699 | |
| | MAGNESIUM: lbs. / acre | Desired Value | 495 | 353 |
| | | Value Found | 417 | 343 |
| | | Deficit | -78 | -10 |
| | POTASSIUM: lbs. / acre | Desired Value | 537 | 383 |
| | | Value Found | 649 | 459 |
| | | Deficit | | |
| | SODIUM: | lbs. / acre | 34 | 31 |
| Base Saturation % | Calcium (60 to 70%) | | 57.84 | 70.64 |
| | Magnesium (10 to 20%) | | 10.09 | 11.63 |
| | Potassium (2 to 5%) | | 4.83 | 4.79 |
| | Sodium (0.5 to 3%) | | 0.44 | 0.54 |
| | Other Bases (Variable) | | 5.80 | 4.90 |
| | Exchangeable Hydrogen (10 to 15%) | | 21.00 | 7.50 |
| Trace Elements | Boron (ppm) | | 0.54 | 0.46 |
| | Iron (ppm) | | 192 | 283 |
| | Manganese (ppm) | | 91 | 113 |
| | Copper (ppm) | | 3.48 | 5.08 |
| | Zinc (ppm) | | 9.53 | 7.61 |
| | Aluminum (ppm) | | 741 | 697 |

**Fig. 60** *The calcium to magnesium ratio in the Laurel sample solution is 10:1 and the magnesium does not meet the threshold amount of 4-8 ppm. In order to balance the solution in the Entire sample, the magnesium should be approximately 7 ppm to meet the 5:1 ratio and bring the percentage numbers close to the 60% calcium and 20% magnesium.*

## High Exchange Capacity Soils Paste Test
## Example 3: Porter Landscaping Samples
## Entire and Laurel

| | | | Porter | Porter |
|---|---|---|---|---|
| Sample Location | | | Porter | Porter |
| Sample Id | | | Laurel | Entire |
| Lab Number | | | 9972 | 9974 |
| Water Used | | | DI | DI |
| pH | | | 5.8 | 6.5 |
| Soluble Salts | | ppm | 394 | 201 |
| Chloride (Cl) | | ppm | 10 | 9 |
| Bicarbonate ($HCO_3$) | | ppm | 107 | 107 |
| Anions | **SULFUR** | ppm | 60.23 | 1.75 |
| | **PHOSPHORUS** | ppm | < 0.1 | < 0.1 |
| Soluble Cations | **CALCIUM** | ppm | 41.77 | 35.82 |
| | | meq/l | 2.09 | 1.79 |
| | **MAGNESIUM** | ppm | 8.26 | 3.35 |
| | | meq/l | 0.69 | 0.28 |
| | **POTASSIUM** | ppm | 45.11 | 15.46 |
| | | meq/l | 1.17 | 0.40 |
| | **SODIUM** | ppm | 8.89 | 4.41 |
| | | meq/l | 0.39 | 0.19 |
| Percent | Calcium | | 48.17 | 67.23 |
| | Magnesium | | 15.88 | 10.49 |
| | Potassium | | 27.03 | 15.07 |
| | Sodium | | 8.92 | 7.20 |
| Trace Elements | Boron (ppm) | | 0.03 | < 0.02 |
| | Iron (ppm) | | 5.07 | 4.05 |
| | Manganese (ppm) | | 1.89 | 0.43 |
| | Copper (ppm) | | < 0.02 | < 0.02 |
| | Zinc (ppm) | | 0.06 | < 0.02 |
| | Aluminum (ppm) | | 9.28 | 9.26 |

**Fig. 61** *The manganese is getting a little high in the Laurel paste test when it comes to turf and general crops. Since the paste test phosphorus came in below the detection limit, it is still wise to attempt to apply half to three-quarters of the phosphorus from crop removal unless the price of phosphorus is abnormally high at application time.*

## High Exchange Capacity Soils Standard Test Example 4: Indiana Baseball Field

Soil test Example 4 is from a baseball field in Indiana that had only a standard test performed on it. The 15.55 m.e. exchange capacity just barely puts it into the high exchange category. Once limed this soil might see this exchange capacity number drop down even as low as 9.5. The magnesium level in the base saturation balance is in the high level, so a high calcium lime would be the lime of choice. I don't want to raise the pH over 6.5, so I would start out with 2,000 lbs. per acre or 50 lbs. per 1,000 ft$^2$ of a 30% calcium lime and then in another year possibly put some gypsum on depending on what a new soil test indicates.

The phosphorus is very low so the addition of lime will not help the solubility of phosphorus, however calcium is important in root development and phosphorus is picked up primarily by diffusion, so the trade off is probably worth it. I would consider putting on a big shot of phosphorus at six weeks prior to liming. I would apply 250-300 lbs. per acre or 6-7 lbs. per 1,000 ft$^2$ of 11-52-0 following an aeration operation. Along with the phosphorus I would also apply 250 lbs. per acre or 6 lbs. per 1,000 ft$^2$ of muriate of potash or potassium sulfate or a combination of the two products. This big shot of phosphorus will tie up some zinc so I would apply 25 lbs. per acre or 0.6 lbs. per 1,000 ft$^2$ of zinc sulfate. It would be preferable to split this into two or three applications. Foliar feeding some zinc and copper would also be a good idea as the buildup applications is being done.

# High Exchange Capacity Soils Standard Test
## Example 4: Indiana Baseball Field

| | | | |
|---|---|---|---|
| Sample Location | | | Baseball |
| Sample ID | | | Field |
| Lab Number | | | 36 |
| Sample Depth (inches) | | | 4 |
| Total Exchange Capacity (m.e.) | | | 15.55 |
| pH of Soil Sample | | | 6.00 |
| Organic Matter (percent) | | | 1.90 |
| **Anions** | SULFUR: | p.p.m. | 15 |
| | Mehlich III Phosphorus: | as ($P_2O_5$) lbs. / acre | 49 |
| **Exchangeable Cations** | CALCIUM: lbs. / acre | Desired Value | 2819 |
| | | Value Found | 2031 |
| | | Deficit | -788 |
| | MAGNESIUM: lbs. / acre | Desired Value | 298 |
| | | Value Found | 694 |
| | | Deficit | |
| | POTASSIUM: lbs. / acre | Desired Value | 323 |
| | | Value Found | 119 |
| | | Deficit | -204 |
| | SODIUM: | lbs. / acre | 60 |
| **Base Saturation %** | Calcium (60 to 70%) | | 48.98 |
| | Magnesium (10 to 20%) | | 27.90 |
| | Potassium (2 to 5%) | | 1.47 |
| | Sodium (0.5 to 3%) | | 1.26 |
| | Other Bases (Variable) | | 5.40 |
| | Exchangeable Hydrogen (10 to 15%) | | 15.00 |
| **Trace Elements** | Boron (ppm) | | 0.41 |
| | Iron (ppm) | | 140 |
| | Manganese (ppm) | | 117 |
| | Copper (ppm) | | 1.12 |
| | Zinc (ppm) | | 0.9 |
| | Aluminum (ppm) | | 797 |

**Fig. 62** *This test shows phosphorus as very low, so the addition of lime will not help the solubility of phosphorus. However, calcium is important in root development and phosphorus is picked up primarily by diffusion, so the trade off is probably worth it.*

## High Exchange Capacity Soils Standard and Paste Test Example 5: Muck Field Samples LS-7 B-W and LS-7 B-E

This is a low pH muck field split into two halves. The exchange capacities are very high due to the 40+ percent organic matter. Looking only at the standard test (Figure 63), one might think that lime is all that is needed to turn this field around. On the contrary, this is a very good field for corn, growing 200+ bushels per acre, however when the field goes to carrots, the east side (LS-7 B-E) invariably ends up yielding less. It is in this crop that the pH becomes the issue, not the calcium or magnesium level. At a pH below 5 the manganese solubility becomes high enough to be toxic, even though the standard test may be as low as 10-15 ppm. In this example all I have to do is apply enough lime to raise the pH above 5 which will lower the solubility of the manganese below 0.20 ppm.

I would start off using 3 tons of dolomite lime, retest a year later, and switch to high calcium if the pH is still too low. Soils with this high of an exchange capacity will have a tremendous buffering capacity so be prepared to use a lot of lime. Don't overdo the lime because this will put pressure on the phosphorus solubility and the potassium retention. There is plenty of soluble calcium and magnesium, even at the 4.8 pH levels. Organic soils do have problems holding potassium, although this sample is not too bad; I would still cover crop removal amounts plus add 100 pounds of 0-0-60 muriate of potash.

Just a quarter mile north of this field the muck is playing out and the high pH marrow is mixing with the muck bringing the pH up to around the 7.5 level. This condition has created manganese as well as a phosphorus deficiency. In organic soils with organic matter above 20 the BCSR balance of 65% calcium and 15% magnesium is not applicable or economically feasible. A balance of 50% calcium and 8% magnesium is probably a good target for a true muck soil, however a transition of this balance for soils with organic matters above 12% and less than 20% needs to be considered. This balance might be closer to 55-60% calcium and 9-10% magnesium. Use the paste testing to verify that enough plant nutrients are soluble but not toxic.

## High Exchange Capacity Soils Standard Test
## Example 5: Muck Field Samples LS-7 B-W and LS-7 B-E

| | | | LS-7 B-W | LS-7 B-E |
|---|---|---|---|---|
| Sample Location | | | | |
| Sample ID | | | | |
| Lab Number | | | 108 | 109 |
| Sample Depth (inches) | | | 9 | 9 |
| Total Exchange Capacity (m.e.) | | | 38.00 | 48.56 |
| pH of Soil Sample | | | 5.10 | 4.80 |
| Organic Matter (percent) | | | 41.33 | 47.59 |
| Anions | SULFUR: | p.p.m. | 65 | 52 |
| | Mehlich III Phosphorus: | as ($P_2O_5$) lbs. / acre | 399 | 481 |
| Exchangeable Cations | CALCIUM: lbs. / acre | Value Found | 9711 | 10335 |
| | MAGNESIUM: lbs. / acre | Value Found | 953 | 1188 |
| | POTASSIUM: lbs. / acre | Value Found | 471 | 449 |
| | SODIUM: | lbs. / acre | 47 | 46 |
| Base Saturation % | Calcium (60 to 70%) | | 42.59 | 35.47 |
| | Magnesium (10 to 20%) | | 6.97 | 6.80 |
| | Potassium (2 to 5%) | | 1.06 | 0.79 |
| | Sodium (0.5 to 3%) | | 0.18 | 0.14 |
| | Other Bases (Variable) | | 7.20 | 7.80 |
| | Exchangeable Hydrogen (10 to 15%) | | 42.00 | 49.00 |
| Trace Elements | Boron (ppm) | | 0.85 | 0.86 |
| | Iron (ppm) | | 58 | 56 |
| | Manganese (ppm) | | 15 | 19 |
| | Copper (ppm) | | 1.52 | 1.29 |
| | Zinc (ppm) | | 3.53 | 4.08 |
| | Aluminum (ppm) | | 92 | 98 |

**Fig. 63** *Soils with this high of an exchange capacity will have a tremendous buffering capacity, so be prepared to use a lot of lime. When growing some crops, such as carrots, pH becomes the issue, not the calcium or magnesium level. At a pH below 5 the manganese solubility becomes high enough to be toxic, even though the standard test may be as low as 10-15 ppm.*

# High Exchange Capacity Soils Paste Test
## Example 5: Muck Field Samples LS-7 B-W and LS-7 B-E

| Sample Location | LS-7 B-W | LS-7 B-E |
|---|---|---|
| Sample Name | | |
| Lab Number | 7208 | 7209 |
| Water Used | DI | DI |
| pH | 5.1 | 4.8 |
| Phosphorus | < 0.1 | 0.1 |
| Calcium | 40.7 | 54 |
| Magnesium | 9.6 | 14.9 |
| Potassium | 10.9 | 10.3 |
| Sodium | 4.1 | 3.9 |
| Sulfur | 34 | 44.1 |
| | | |
| Boron | 0.08 | 0.09 |
| Iron | 1.24 | 1.18 |
| Manganese | 0.16 | 0.26 |
| Copper | 0.02 | < 0.02 |
| Zinc | < 0.02 | 0.07 |
| Aluminum | 1.95 | 2.17 |
| Molybdenum | < 0.01 | < 0.01 |
| Cobalt | < 0.01 | < 0.01 |
| | | |
| Calcium % | 62.3% | 65.0% |
| Magnesium % | 14.7% | 17.9% |
| Potassium % | 16.7% | 12.4% |
| Sodium % | 6.2% | 4.7% |
| | | |
| Calcium %:Magnesium % | 4.2 | 3.6 |
| | | |
| Calcium mEq/L | 2.03 | 2.70 |
| Magnesium mEq/L | 3.39 | 4.50 |
| Potassium mEq/L | 1.07 | 1.42 |
| Sodium mEq/L | 1.85 | 2.45 |

**Fig. 64** *A balance of 50% calcium and 8% magnesium is probably a good target for a true muck soil like this example, however a transition of this balance for soils with organic matter levels between 12% and 20% needs to be considered. This balance might be closer to 55-60% calcium and 9-10% magnesium. Use paste testing to verify that enough plant nutrients are soluble and present but not toxic.*

## High Exchange Capacity Soils Standard and Paste Test Example 6: McGuffy Muck Sample TS-1

This sample was taken from an area known as the McGuffy Muck. It is in an area where the muck has oxidized to the point that only a few inches is left and the marrow subsoil has been worked into the muck. The marrow subsoil has a very high pH. It is loaded with prehistoric snail shells and free calcium carbonate. The standard test appears to have extracted excess calcium (Figure 65).

The phosphorus results are abnormally low. It seems that the extracting solution may have been neutralized to some degree by the calcareous marrow. The low phosphorus result on the standard test is not verified by the paste test. Although the phosphorus is still low on the paste test (Figure 66), it is not below the detection limit as you might expect from the extremely low level on the standard test. On this soil I would try to concentrate a large portion of my phosphorus in starter or a row application since the pH and the calcium levels are so high.

Potassium and magnesium are low in both tests. K-Mag would be the nutrient of choice supplying both nutrients in one product. I would try to incorporate 250-300 lbs. per acre of K-Mag and follow up with tissue sampling and another soil sample next year to see what impact was made on the soil.

If a magnesium source such as K-Mag or magnesium oxysulfate were not available, I would consider using 1-2 tons of dolomite lime to initiate a better balance. The pH would not go up much further, but the solubility of the lime would be very low. If a dolomite lime is used to improve the magnesium balance, remember to follow up with a paste test six months to a year later. This would allow you to see what really is happening in solution since the Mehlich extraction solution could dissolve the lime, artificially making the standard test look good.

Most of the trace elements are very low in the paste test.

I would tissue test the growing crops, especially at critical stages such as the early vegetative growth and flowering stages, in an attempt to determine a foliar program. Remember plants tend to grow to the least available nutrient so experimenting with trace elements that produce a known response to a particular crop is still a good idea.

# High Exchange Capacity Soils Standard Test Example 6: McGuffy Muck Sample TS-1

| | | | TS-1 |
|---|---|---|---|
| Sample Location | | | TS-1 |
| Sample ID | | | B-W |
| Lab Number | | | 40 |
| Sample Depth (inches) | | | 9 |
| Total Exchange Capacity (m.e.) | | | 38.30 |
| pH of Soil Sample | | | 7.30 |
| Organic Matter (percent) | | | 17.17 |
| **Anions** | **SULFUR:** | p.p.m. | 76 |
| | **Mehlich III Phosphorus:** | as ($P_2O_5$) lbs. / acre | 46 |
| **Exchangeable Cations** | **CALCIUM:** lbs. / acre | Value Found | 20454 |
| | **MAGNESIUM:** lbs. / acre | Value Found | 783 |
| | **POTASSIUM:** lbs. / acre | Value Found | 485 |
| | **SODIUM:** | lbs. / acre | 35 |
| **Base Saturation %** | Calcium (60 to 70%) | | 89.01 |
| | Magnesium (10 to 20%) | | 5.68 |
| | Potassium (2 to 5%) | | 1.08 |
| | Sodium (0.5 to 3%) | | 0.13 |
| | Other Bases (Variable) | | 4.10 |
| | Exchangeable Hydrogen (10 to 15%) | | 0.00 |
| **Trace Elements** | Boron (ppm) | | 1.04 |
| | Iron (ppm) | | 212 |
| | Manganese (ppm) | | 27 |
| | Copper (ppm) | | 6.76 |
| | Zinc (ppm) | | 3.14 |
| | Aluminum (ppm) | | 124 |

**Fig. 65** *The standard test appears to have extracted excess calcium. The phosphorus results are abnormally low. It seems that the extracting solution may have been neutralized to some degree by the calcareous marrow. The low phosphorus result on the standard test is not verified by the paste test.*

# High Exchange Capacity Soils Paste Test
## Example 6: McGuffy Muck Sample TS-1

| | |
|---|---|
| Sample Location | TS-1 |
| Sample Name | B-W |
| Lab Number | 7135 |
| Water Used | DI |
| pH | 7.3 |
| Phosphorus | 0.2 |
| Calcium | 42.8 |
| Magnesium | 3.4 |
| Potassium | 6.9 |
| Sodium | 2.4 |
| Sulfur | 16.1 |
| Boron | < 0.02 |
| Iron | 1.38 |
| Manganese | < 0.02 |
| Copper | 0.02 |
| Zinc | < 0.02 |
| Aluminum | 2.44 |
| Molybdenum | 1.45 |
| Cobalt | < 0.01 |
| Calcium % | 77.1% |
| Magnesium % | 6.2% |
| Potassium % | 12.4% |
| Sodium % | 4.3% |
| Calcium %:Magnesium % | 12.5 |
| Calcium mEq/L | 2.14 |
| Magnesium mEq/L | 3.57 |
| Potassium mEq/L | 1.13 |
| Sodium mEq/L | 1.95 |

**Fig. 66** *Although phosphorus is still low on this paste test, it is not below the detection limit like you might expect with the extremely low level on the standard test. Most of the trace elements are very low in the paste test.*

# High Exchange Capacity Soils Standard and Paste Test Example 7: Northwest Ohio Sample DM-2B

This sample was collected in northwest Ohio. The field is located in a creek bottom and the soil is a black, heavy soil. The 18.08 level for exchange capacity puts it in this section of soils to be balanced using the BCSR method. The pH at 5.7 and the base saturation indicates that we should lime this soil, but the question is "What kind of lime should we use?" The standard test would lead us to choose a high calcium lime since the magnesium is close to the 15% desired level and the calcium is almost 12 points from the desired 65%. The paste test shows the calcium is about one-third of what the desired level should be and the magnesium is about half of the desired level. If a high calcium lime is used, the calcium would certainly improve, but it might reduce the magnesium availability to the plants. Ideally it would be nice to find a lime that is somewhere between a high calcium and a dolomite lime. I have seen analysis of limes with around 25% calcium and 7% magnesium, but they are not very common. When being forced to choose from between a high calcium and dolomitic lime, I would start out with a light dolomite lime application of 1,500-2,000 lbs. per acre. Initially this would cover both the calcium and magnesium levels in solution. Soil testing 12 months later would show whether more lime is needed or an application of gypsum. This process makes a huge assumption that the initial lime application would be incorporated and not left on top. If the lime is left on top, it is even more important that the initial application be small and a fine (70%+ passing through a 100-mesh screen) lime. This will allow the lime to completely break down and move into solution.

Remember calcium is taken up and transported through the xylem, so it is one directional in the plant. Calcium in the topsoil layers cannot do anything to help root development in the lower levels. This is one of the reasons that I believe a true no-tiller should be soil sampling the top 0-2 inch layer separately and maintaining the soil pH only between 6.2 and 6.5. Anything higher reduces the breakdown of limes and affects nutrient solubility.

The phosphorus and potassium are low in both the standard and paste test so buildup applications will be needed. I would cover the removal rates along with a 25% increase (see nutrient removal chart for corn, beans and wheat in Figure 69).

The removal rates for turfgrass could be calculated from a tissue analysis and by knowing the weight and amounts of clippings removed from the greens and tees. This method could also be used for many other crops from apples to spinach.

The traces on the standard test are low in manganese and zinc, however this is quite the opposite on the paste test. Manganese and zinc are adequate on the paste test and copper is low. Copper is picked up in the plant mostly by direct root intercept. Notice how low the calcium is in solution. Knowing the importance of calcium in root development, copper would be my top concern.

The feed rates of manganese and zinc into solution could be low since they're levels are low on the standard test. Tissue sampling will be the best method to sort this quandary out.

## High Exchange Capacity Soils Standard Test
## Example 7: Northwest Ohio Sample DM-2B

| Sample Location | | | DM-2B |
|---|---|---|---|
| | | | |
| Lab Number | | | 54 |
| Sample Depth (inches) | | | 9 |
| Total Exchange Capacity (m.e.) | | | 18.08 |
| pH of Soil Sample | | | 5.70 |
| Organic Matter (percent) | | | 3.78 |
| **Anions** | **SULFUR:** | p.p.m. | 18 |
| | **Mehlich III Phosphorus:** | as ($P_2O_5$) lbs. / acre | 159 |
| **Exchangeable Cations** | **CALCIUM:** lbs. / acre | Value Found | 5805 |
| | **MAGNESIUM:** lbs. / acre | Value Found | 929 |
| | **POTASSIUM:** lbs. / acre | Value Found | 386 |
| | **SODIUM:** | lbs. / acre | 46 |
| **Base Saturation %** | Calcium (60 to 70%) | | 53.52 |
| | Magnesium (10 to 20%) | | 14.28 |
| | Potassium (2 to 5%) | | 1.83 |
| | Sodium (0.5 to 3%) | | 0.37 |
| | Other Bases (Variable) | | 6.00 |
| | Exchangeable Hydrogen (10 to 15%) | | 24.00 |
| **Trace Elements** | Boron (ppm) | | 0.68 |
| | Iron (ppm) | | 302 |
| | Manganese (ppm) | | 12 |
| | Copper (ppm) | | 3.58 |
| | Zinc (ppm) | | 1.57 |
| | Aluminum (ppm) | | 909 |

**Fig. 67** *The standard test suggests a high calcium lime since the magnesium is close to the 15% desired level and the calcium is almost 12 points from the desired 65%. The phosphorus and potassium levels are low in both the standard and paste test so buildup applications will be needed.*

# High Exchange Capacity Soils Paste Test
## Example 7: Northwest Ohio Sample DM-2B

| Sample Location | DM-2B |
|---|---|
| | |
| Lab Number | 7185 |
| Water Used | DI |
| | |
| pH | 5.7 |
| | |
| Phosphorus | < 0.1 |
| Calcium | 8.7 |
| Magnesium | 3 |
| Potassium | 4.5 |
| Sodium | 3.4 |
| Sulfur | 6.9 |
| | |
| Boron | 0.21 |
| Iron | 4.57 |
| Manganese | 0.07 |
| Copper | < 0.02 |
| Zinc | 0.06 |
| Aluminum | 8.09 |
| Molybdenum | < 0.01 |
| Cobalt | < 0.01 |
| | |
| Calcium % | 44.3% |
| Magnesium % | 15.2% |
| Potassium % | 22.9% |
| Sodium % | 17.5% |
| | |
| Calcium %:Magnesium % | 2.9 |
| | |
| Calcium mEq/L | 0.43 |
| Magnesium mEq/L | 0.72 |
| Potassium mEq/L | 0.23 |
| Sodium mEq/L | 0.39 |

**Fig. 68** *The paste test shows the calcium is about one-third of what the desired level should be and the magnesium is about half of the desired level. The traces on the standard test are low in manganese and zinc, however this is quite the opposite on the paste test. Manganese and zinc are adequate on the paste test and copper is low.*

# Crop Removal Chart for Corn, Beans and Wheat

### Corn Nutrient Removal

| Bushels | 100 | 110 | 120 | 130 | 140 | 150 | 160 | 170 | 180 | 190 | 200 | 210 |
|---|---|---|---|---|---|---|---|---|---|---|---|---|
| **Nutrient** | | | | | | | | | | | | |
| **Phosphorus** | 40 | 44 | 48 | 52 | 56 | 66 | 64 | 68 | 72 | 76 | 80 | 84 |
| 18-46-0 | 83 | 92 | 104 | 113 | 122 | 131 | 140 | 148 | 156 | 165 | 174 | 183 |
| 11-52-0 | 77 | 85 | 92 | 100 | 108 | 115 | 123 | 131 | 138 | 146 | 154 | 162 |
| **Potassium** | 25 | 27.5 | 30 | 32.5 | 35 | 37.5 | 40 | 42.5 | 45 | 47.5 | 50 | 52.5 |
| 0-0-60 | 42 | 46 | 50 | 54 | 58 | 62 | 66 | 70 | 74 | 78 | 82 | 86 |

### Soybean Nutrient Removal

| Bushels | 30 | 35 | 40 | 45 | 50 | 55 | 60 | 65 | 70 | 75 | 80 | 85 |
|---|---|---|---|---|---|---|---|---|---|---|---|---|
| **Nutrient** | | | | | | | | | | | | |
| **Phosphorus** | 27 | 31 | 36 | 40 | 45 | 49 | 54 | 56 | 62 | 67 | 72 | 76 |
| 18-46-0 | 59 | 67 | 78 | 87 | 98 | 106 | 117 | 125 | 135 | 146 | 156 | 165 |
| 11-52-0 | 52 | 60 | 69 | 77 | 86 | 95 | 103 | 112 | 120 | 129 | 137 | 146 |
| **Potassium** | 39 | 45 | 52 | 58 | 65 | 71 | 78 | 84 | 91 | 97 | 104 | 110 |
| 0-0-60 | 65 | 75 | 87 | 97 | 108 | 118 | 130 | 140 | 150 | 162 | 174 | 183 |

### Wheat Nutrient Removal

| Bushels | 50 | 55 | 60 | 65 | 70 | 75 | 80 | 85 | 90 | 95 | 100 | 110 |
|---|---|---|---|---|---|---|---|---|---|---|---|---|
| **Nutrient** | | | | | | | | | | | | |
| **Phosphorus** | | | | | | | | | | | | |
| 18-46-0 | 57 | 63 | 68 | 74 | 80 | 86 | 91 | 97 | 103 | 108 | 114 | 120 |
| 11-52-0 | 53 | 58 | 64 | 69 | 74 | 80 | 85 | 90 | 95 | 101 | 106 | 111 |
| **Potassium** | | | | | | | | | | | | |
| 0-0-60 | 53 | 58 | 64 | 69 | 74 | 80 | 85 | 90 | 95 | 101 | 106 | 111 |

Note: These calculations are based on a moisture-free basis so they are conservative and allow for minimal erosion loss. Results in pounds per acre removal in oxide form.

**Fig. 69** *Crop nutrient removal rates for corn, beans and wheat crops, given in pounds per acre removal in oxide form.*

## High Exchange Capacity Soils Standard and Paste Test Example 8: Baseball Infield Sample

Example 8 is a sample collected from a newly installed baseball field at a small university. The installation was contracted out to a firm that did the grading, fertilization, sodding and irrigation installation. The site looked very nice when they were done, but it turns out that a few problems were looming under the surface, literally. As far as I know the installation firm did not enquire about the quality of the water used to irrigate this field. The water has a high pH of 7.4 with bicarbonate levels around 400 and a salt concentration of nearly 500. Drainage becomes critical especially with water quality this bad. I have seen water much worse, but most of those samples were associated with very sandy soils. This infield needs to drain and by looking at the sulfur level on either the standard (Figure 70) or the paste test (Figure 71), the high level indicates that it is not draining. The high magnesium level in the standard test contributes to the tightness of the soil. The sodium is high and the irrigation water with only 31 ppm will only add to this problem since drainage is poor. Running short cycles of irrigation will speed up the sodium accumulation and consequently the dispersion of the clay particles. Without addressing the drainage issues with tile or some sort of subsurface drainage the success with this infield will be very limited.

The soil selected for the base of this baseball infield should have had chemistry and physical testing done—especially percolation rates preformed on it prior to moving it into place. Using surfactants may help a little bit, but that is only treating the symptom and not the problem. In an attempt to readjust the balance with gypsum and extra potassium, you will add to an already high salts level and potentially make the situation worse. Based on the paste test results (Figure 71) the high pH is tying up the phosphorus, but it may also be helping another potential problem and that is boron. The standard test shows boron in a potentially toxic range, but the paste test suggests that a lot of the boron may be tied up with calcium. Dropping the pH down rapidly without flushing boron in the process might create some boron toxicity issues.

Another subtle indication of the drainage problem is the manganese level found in the paste test. Normally at this high pH the manganese would be below the detection limit. Manganese becomes more soluble in a reducing environment such as saturated soils. The high pH did depress the zinc and copper solubility down to the detection limits.

Oftentimes as an agronomist you can't tell your client to fix the drainage and then I'll help you out. In this situation I would start early spring with an application of a good soil surfactant and a humic acid product, either liquid or dry. The idea of the humic acid would be to help increase biological activity and increase the availability of my fertilizer applications. Even though the fertilizer levels are very good in the standard test, an application of 11-52-0 at 5 lbs. per 1,000 ft$^2$ and 0-0-60 at 4 lbs. per 1,000 ft$^2$ would add some soluble nutrition during the cold, wet spring. I would use a foliar program with a chelated copper and zinc at greenup the turfgrass and continue through the season. Getting timely, light rain showers would also be a help too.

# High Exchange Capacity Soils Standard Test
## Example 8: Baseball Infield Sample

| Sample Location | | | Infield |
|---|---|---|---|
| | | | |
| Lab Number | | | 45 |
| Sample Depth (inches) | | | 9 |
| Total Exchange Capacity (m.e.) | | | 27.25 |
| pH of Soil Sample | | | 7.50 |
| Organic Matter (percent) | | | 7.47 |
| **Anions** | **SULFUR:** | p.p.m. | 327 |
| | **Mehlich III Phosphorus:** | as ($P_2O_5$) lbs. / acre | 708 |
| **Exchangeable Cations** | **CALCIUM:** lbs. / acre | Value Found | 10978 |
| | **MAGNESIUM:** lbs. / acre | Value Found | 2597 |
| | **POTASSIUM:** lbs. / acre | Value Found | 573 |
| | **SODIUM:** | lbs. / acre | 130 |
| **Base Saturation %** | Calcium (60 to 70%) | | 67.15 |
| | Magnesium (10 to 20%) | | 26.47 |
| | Potassium (2 to 5%) | | 1.80 |
| | Sodium (0.5 to 3%) | | 0.69 |
| | Other Bases (Variable) | | 3.90 |
| | Exchangeable Hydrogen (10 to 15%) | | 0.00 |
| **Trace Elements** | Boron (ppm) | | 4 |
| | Iron (ppm) | | 330 |
| | Manganese (ppm) | | 45 |
| | Copper (ppm) | | 3.37 |
| | Zinc (ppm) | | 14.65 |
| | Aluminum (ppm) | | 681 |

**Fig. 70** *The high magnesium level in the standard test contributes to the tightness of the soil. The high sulfur level indicates that this soil is not draining. Without addressing the drainage issues with tile or some sort of subsurface drainage the success with this infield will be very limited.*

# High Exchange Capacity Soils Paste Test
## Example 8: Baseball Infield Sample

| Sample Location | | | Infield |
|---|---|---|---|
| | | | |
| Lab Number | | | 11379 |
| Water Used | | | DI |
| pH | | | 7.5 |
| Soluble Salts | | ppm | 827 |
| Chloride (Cl) | | ppm | 7 |
| Bicarbonate (HCO$_3$) | | ppm | 298 |
| Anions | SULFUR | ppm | 152.4 |
| | PHOSPHORUS | ppm | < 0.1 |
| Soluble Cations | CALCIUM | ppm | 99.84 |
| | | meq/l | 4.99 |
| | MAGNESIUM | ppm | 31.88 |
| | | meq/l | 2.66 |
| | POTASSIUM: | ppm | 13.05 |
| | | meq/l | 0.34 |
| | SODIUM | ppm | 20.95 |
| | | meq/l | 0.91 |
| Percent | Calcium | | 56.10 |
| | Magnesium | | 29.86 |
| | Potassium | | 3.81 |
| | Sodium | | 10.24 |
| Trace Elements | Boron (ppm) | | 0.57 |
| | Iron (ppm) | | 2.24 |
| | Manganese (ppm) | | 0.12 |
| | Copper (ppm) | | < 0.02 |
| | Zinc (ppm) | | 0.02 |
| | Aluminum (ppm) | | 6 |

**Fig. 71** *Based on the paste test results, the high pH is tying up the phosphorus but it may also be helping another potential problem and that is boron. The paste test suggests that a lot of the boron may be tied up with calcium.*

## High Exchange Capacity Soils Standard and Paste Test Example 9: Ohio Farm Sample Field B

This field is from an 80-acre farm. Over the last 25 years Field B has probably been in hay more than 60% of the time. This farm lies at the edge of Ohio's lakebed soils and has a high clay content. Changing the balance on these soils is a slow and arduous task. Some might even say it is a foolish task to try and change the balance on these heavy clays. Thinking that you could change these soils in five years, is a foolhardy idea. For these heavy soils with slow internal drainage I believe approaching these soils realizing that this is a long-term commitment is important. The soils are not going to be consistently high yielding. Given the right conditions, these soils will do very well especially in droughty conditions.

Compaction is a huge problem since these soils don't dry out well in the spring. Compaction issues will start in the fall with harvest and carry over to the next year crop. Freezing and thawing will not remove compaction in one year. Compaction is nothing more than squeezing the air and pore space out of the soil. In order to expand and break up the compaction layer there must be pore space filled with water, so in the process of freezing, the water will expand and start to fracture the compacted area. Controlled traffic and vertical tillage can make all but especially heavy soils more productive.

It is the heavy soils that are adversely affected most often from having high magnesium levels. High magnesium soils tend to compact easier, run together and seal over. Weed pressure on this soil type tends to be highest in the area of grasses rather than broadleaf weeds. In this example, Field B is already very high in magnesium.

Twenty-five years ago when I started with this client the magnesium was over 35% with a pH of 7.5. We have lowered the magnesium percentage by nearly 20%, but lowering magnesium was not our primary objective. The subsoil clay is so dense that even if we could free up magnesium, there was really nowhere for it to go. The magnesium level has dropped primarily because of crop removal.

When we did need lime, high calcium was used. When calcium

solubility was needed, like it is in this example, gypsum was used. An interesting point comes from comments made by the farmer. He feels that it now takes less horsepower to farm the ground and the ground doesn't stick to the tires as bad. I can attest to the last comment. I have always done most of my sampling from a four-wheeler. I sampled uneventfully this fall in rather wet conditions, but had it been 20 years ago I would still be cleaning the mud out of my four-wheeler's tires weeks later.

In this example the pH is where it should be, but the calcium solubility is low so I would use 1,000-1,200 lbs. of gypsum per acre. The magnesium is low in solubility (Figure 73), but this is quite common. Applying gypsum will displace some of the magnesium on the colloid and bring it into solution, making it available for plant uptake or leaching if there is internal drainage.

Dropping the magnesium level on a high pH and high magnesium soil is very slow at first. If the pH is above 7, there is a good chance that there is undissolved dolomitic lime in the soil. Therefore as magnesium is removed from the colloid and the soil system the reserve lime can dissolve and replace the displaced magnesium. It is like taking a glass of water and stirring in salt or sugar until the water can hold no more and the granules begin to accumulate at the bottom. If you measure the salt or sugar content in the water with a meter it will produce a specific value, lets say 100. Pouring a little water out of the glass and replacing it with fresh water will cause some of the granules on the bottom of the glass to dissolve but the salt or sugar content in the water will continue to read 100 until all the granules are dissolved. Once all the granules are dissolved, pouring a little water out again and replacing it with fresh water will cause the meter readings to change to something under 100. Although the potassium is high on the standard test, it is very low in the paste test. This is common in the high clay soils. Tissue samples tend to substantiate the poor flow rates into solution. Besides poor flow rates, the heavy soils have more compaction and less root development which exacerbates this problem. Spring applications of potassium have yielded better tissue numbers over fall applications. Keep potassium in your foliar programs.

# High Exchange Capacity Soils Standard Test
## Example 9: Ohio Farm Sample Field B

| | | |
|---|---|---|
| Sample Location | | 1 |
| Sample ID | | Field B |
| Lab Number | | 86 |
| Sample Depth (inches) | | 9 |
| Total Exchange Capacity (m.e.) | | 18.97 |
| pH of Soil Sample | | 6.50 |
| Organic Matter (percent) | | 3.11 |
| **Anions** | **SULFUR:** p.p.m. | 15 |
| | **Mehlich III Phosphorus:** as ($P_2O_5$) lbs. / acre | 114 |
| **Exchangeable Cations** | **CALCIUM:** lbs. / acre    Value Found | 6420 |
| | **MAGNESIUM:** lbs. / acre    Value Found | 1907 |
| | **POTASSIUM:** lbs. / acre    Value Found | 608 |
| | **SODIUM:** lbs. / acre | 66 |
| **Base Saturation %** | Calcium (60 to 70%) | 56.42 |
| | Magnesium (10 to 20%) | 27.93 |
| | Potassium (2 to 5%) | 2.74 |
| | Sodium (0.5 to 3%) | 0.51 |
| | Other Bases (Variable) | 4.90 |
| | Exchangeable Hydrogen (10 to 15%) | 7.50 |
| **Trace Elements** | Boron (ppm) | 0.93 |
| | Iron (ppm) | 284 |
| | Manganese (ppm) | 37 |
| | Copper (ppm) | 2.1 |
| | Zinc (ppm) | 3.35 |
| | Aluminum (ppm) | 914 |

**Fig. 72** *In this example the pH is where it should be, but the calcium solubility is low.*

# High Exchange Capacity Soils Paste Test
## Example 9: Ohio Farm Sample Field B

| | |
|---|---|
| Sample Location | 1 |
| Sample Name | Field B |
| Lab Number | 6386 |
| Water Used | DI |
| | |
| pH | 6.5 |
| | |
| Phosphorus | < 0.1 |
| Calcium | 12 |
| Magnesium | 4.1 |
| Potassium | 3.9 |
| Sodium | 4.6 |
| Sulfur | 2.6 |
| | |
| Boron | 0.08 |
| Iron | 3.13 |
| Manganese | 0.03 |
| Copper | 0.02 |
| Zinc | < 0.02 |
| Aluminum | 6.56 |
| Molybdenum | 0.13 |
| Cobalt | < 0.01 |
| | |
| Calcium % | 48.7% |
| Magnesium % | 16.7% |
| Potassium % | 15.7% |
| Sodium % | 18.8% |
| | |
| Calcium %:Magnesium % | 2.9 |
| | |
| Calcium mEq/L | 0.60 |
| Magnesium mEq/L | 1.00 |
| Potassium mEq/L | 0.32 |
| Sodium mEq/L | 0.55 |

**Fig. 73** *Field B shows that the magnesium is low in solubility, but this is quite common. Applying gypsum will displace some of the magnesium on the colloid and bring it into solution, making it available for plant uptake or leaching if there is internal drainage.*

## High Exchange Capacity Soils Standard and Paste Test Example 10: Northwest Ohio Farm Samples MW-1A and MW-2 A-W

The two soils in Example 10 are from a northwest Ohio farm representing roughly 70 acres. Corn, beans and wheat are the rotational crops planted on the farm. An earlier sample test done showed the paste test results for the two samples to be 29% calcium and 39% magnesium. The soils are light in color and tend to seal over and run together after a rain event. The soil pH using the standard test is high for sample MW-1A and right where it should be for MW-2 A-W (Figure 74). The pH values did not vary much from the previous sample results.

Prior to this sampling, approximately 1,200 lbs. per acre of gypsum was applied to sample MW-1A. Maintenance fertilizer was applied to both fields. The gypsum did a nice job of increasing the solubility of calcium and even bumping off about 4 ppm of magnesium when the results were compared to the previous test.

The phosphorus and potassium are low in both samples. Buildup applications of at least 200 lbs. per acre each of MAP and 0-0-60 would be a good start, but this still is a long way from fixing the problem. Taking some of the phosphorus out of the broadcast and placing it in the row as a dry or liquid equivalent would improve crop uptake efficiency. I would prefer to apply this fertilizer program every year until there is improvement on the soil tests. MW-2 A-W should also get a 1,000-1,200 lb. per acre application of gypsum.

The trace elements are poor with the exception of iron and manganese. An application of 10 lbs. per acre of 10% boron, 5 pounds per acre of copper sulfate, and 15-20 lbs. per acre of zinc sulfate should also be included in the broadcast application. This application of traces may be a somewhat questionable thing to do, since much of the trace elements could be tied up in the soil. This is also true for the phosphorus and potassium, but broadcasting phosphorus and potassium has been a common practice and a more acceptable thing to do. The traces could be foliar fed, however the soil levels will never improve. The major elements could also be foliar fed to nurse the crop through critical growth stages but it would not be economical to depend solely upon foliar feeding for all the crops phosphorus and potassium needs.

With the amount of fertilizer being applied along with the gypsum, an aggressive tillage program should be used to incorporate the nutrients 6-8 inches deep. This would also include the use of cover crops to prevent soil and nutrient loss. When the soils finally return to an acceptable fertility level, the tillage could be reduced even to the point of no-till. Since the trace elements of boron, copper and zinc are so low in the solubility test, the ideal situation would be to cut back on some of the broadcast applications and to foliar feed at critical times.

If this soil analysis came from an existing turf site that could not be tilled, the overall fertility program could still be used but implemented in different ways. The incorporation would have to come from core aerating and topdressing. The core aeration would have to be rather aggressive, and the topdress material would have to be pretested and the fertility level adjusted prior to being topdressed and swept into the cores. Adjusting the topdress to be 25-30% higher than the desired levels found in Figure 10 would help to improve the soil that is in proximity to the cores, albeit the ensuing diffusion is not going to move the nutrients very far. Using organics such as humate products would help to hold the fertility in a nutrient-rich topdress, in addition to boosting the biological activity.

# High Exchange Capacity Soils Standard Test
# Example 10: Northwest Ohio Farm Samples
# MW-1A and MW-2 A-W

| Sample Location | | | MW-1A | MW-2 A-W |
|---|---|---|---|---|
| Sample ID | | | | |
| Lab Number | | | 61 | 64 |
| Sample Depth (inches) | | | 9 | 9 |
| Total Exchange Capacity (m.e.) | | | 13.55 | 10.37 |
| pH of Soil Sample | | | 6.90 | 6.20 |
| Organic Matter (percent) | | | 3.36 | 3.16 |
| Anions | SULFUR: | p.p.m. | 17 | 4 |
| | Mehlich III Phosphorus: | as ($P_2O_5$) lbs. / acre | 52 | 55 |
| Exchangeable Cations | CALCIUM: lbs. / acre | Value Found | 5583 | 3885 |
| | MAGNESIUM: lbs. / acre | Value Found | 1131 | 673 |
| | POTASSIUM: lbs. / acre | Value Found | 271 | 237 |
| | SODIUM: | lbs. / acre | 43 | 28 |
| Base Saturation % | Calcium (60 to 70%) | | 68.66 | 62.44 |
| | Magnesium (10 to 20%) | | 23.18 | 18.03 |
| | Potassium (2 to 5%) | | 1.71 | 1.95 |
| | Sodium (0.5 to 3%) | | 0.46 | 0.39 |
| | Other Bases (Variable) | | 4.50 | 5.20 |
| | Exchangeable Hydrogen (10 to 15%) | | 1.50 | 12.00 |
| Trace Elements | Boron (ppm) | | 0.5 | 0.48 |
| | Iron (ppm) | | 125 | 140 |
| | Manganese (ppm) | | 85 | 32 |
| | Copper (ppm) | | 1.34 | 1.07 |
| | Zinc (ppm) | | 0.76 | 0.97 |
| | Aluminum (ppm) | | 640 | 702 |

**Fig. 74** *The soil pH with the standard test is high for the MW-1A sample and right where it should be on the MW-2 A-W sample. The phosphorus and potassium are low in both samples. The trace elements are poor with the exception of iron and manganese.*

# High Exchange Capacity Soils Paste Test
## Example 10: Northwest Ohio Farm Samples
## MW-1A and MW-2 A-W

| Sample Location | MW-1A | MW-2 A-W |
|---|---|---|
| Sample Name | | |
| Lab Number | 7147 | 7148 |
| Water Used | DI | DI |
| | | |
| pH | 6.9 | 6.2 |
| | | |
| Phosphorus | < 0.1 | 0.1 |
| Calcium | 29.4 | 11.9 |
| Magnesium | 10.8 | 4.5 |
| Potassium | 6.5 | 5 |
| Sodium | 3.7 | 3.1 |
| Sulfur | 11.2 | 2.5 |
| | | |
| Boron | 0.03 | 0.03 |
| Iron | 1.03 | 7.85 |
| Manganese | 0.1 | 0.08 |
| Copper | < 0.02 | < 0.02 |
| Zinc | 0.02 | 0.02 |
| Aluminum | 1.76 | 1.44 |
| Molybdenum | < 0.01 | < 0.01 |
| Cobalt | < 0.01 | < 0.01 |
| | | |
| Calcium % | 58.3% | 48.6% |
| Magnesium % | 21.4% | 18.4% |
| Potassium % | 12.9% | 20.2% |
| Sodium % | 7.4% | 12.8% |
| | | |
| Calcium %:Magnesium % | 2.7 | 2.6 |
| | | |
| Calcium mEq/L | 1.47 | 0.60 |
| Magnesium mEq/L | 2.45 | 1.00 |
| Potassium mEq/L | 0.77 | 0.31 |
| Sodium mEq/L | 1.34 | 0.54 |

**Fig. 75** *Since the trace elements of boron, copper and zinc are so low in the solubility test, the ideal situation would be to cut back on some of the broadcast applications and to foliar feed at critical times. The traces could be foliar fed, however the soil levels will never improve.*

## High Exchange Capacity Soils Standard and Paste Test Example 11: Farm Field A-E Sample

This example is a field that has received a large amount of biosolids blended with a waste lime product. This field is set up to grow corn, beans and wheat on rotation. Yields are a struggle to reach: 50 bushels per acre for wheat, 45 bushels per acre for beans and 130 bushels per acre for corn, unless the weather is extremely wet.

At first glance most farmers would be watering at the mouth for the fertility levels on the standard soil report (Figure 76). Studying the paste test though shows quite a different picture (Figure 77). The nutrient availability is quite low on the paste test. Phosphorus, along with manganese, copper and zinc, are below the detection limit (<0.02) in spite of the extremely high levels on the standard report. Corn yields on this field will suffer a 15-20 bushel yield loss if 10 gallons per acre of liquid ammonium polyphosphate (10-34-0) is not used in the starter fertilizer.

The problem is quite simple. The high pH and excess calcium is rendering many of the nutrients unavailable. The exchange capacity is probably overstated by 20-25% due the excess calcium dissolved in the extraction process.

Tissue analysis frequently shows trace element deficiencies as well as phosphorus and potassium deficiencies.

In addition, wheat suffers an extreme population loss from take-all disease in part due to manganese deficiency. Wheat and soybeans do much better when planted into a more compact seedbed. This is primarily due to the increased manganese availability.

The fix for this soil is primarily in treating the symptom and not the problem. Until the excess calcium is gone and the pH drops below 7, hedging against induced deficiencies is the best strategy that one can expect. About all that can be done nutritionally is to use row starters for corn and beans as well as foliar feeding of trace elements and adding some phosphorus and potassium during critical demand times.

Glyphosate should be avoided as much as possible due to the tie up effect of the trace elements, especially manganese. This will be very difficult since the organic matter in this soil is very high and the weed pressure is also very high.

# High Exchange Capacity Soils Standard Test
## Example 11: Farm Field A-E Sample

| Sample Location | | Field |
|---|---|---|
| Sample ID | | A-E |
| Lab Number | | 127 |
| Sample Depth (inches) | | 9 |
| Total Exchange Capacity (m.e.) | | 28.12 |
| pH of Soil Sample | | 7.60 |
| Organic Matter (percent) | | 8.86 |
| **Anions** | **SULFUR:** p.p.m. | 52 |
| | **Mehlich III Phosphorus:** as ($P_2O_5$) lbs. / acre | 1340 |
| **Exchangeable Cations** | **CALCIUM:** lbs. / acre        Value Found | 11876 |
| | **MAGNESIUM:** lbs. / acre        Value Found | 2294 |
| | **POTASSIUM:** lbs. / acre        Value Found | 906 |
| | **SODIUM:** lbs. / acre | 80 |
| **Base Saturation %** | Calcium (60 to 70%) | 70.38 |
| | Magnesium (10 to 20%) | 22.66 |
| | Potassium (2 to 5%) | 2.75 |
| | Sodium (0.5 to 3%) | 0.41 |
| | Other Bases (Variable) | 3.80 |
| | Exchangeable Hydrogen (10 to 15%) | 0.00 |
| **Trace Elements** | Boron (ppm) | 2.45 |
| | Iron (ppm) | 281 |
| | Manganese (ppm) | 32 |
| | Copper (ppm) | 6.45 |
| | Zinc (ppm) | 21.42 |
| | Aluminum (ppm) | 1164 |

**Fig. 76** *At first glance most farmers would be watering at the mouth for the fertility levels on the standard soil report. The high pH and excess calcium in this sample though is rendering many of the nutrients unavailable. The exchange capacity is probably overstated by 20-25% due the excess calcium dissolved in the extraction process.*

# High Exchange Capacity Soils Paste Test
## Example 11: Farm Field A-E Sample

| Sample Location | Field |
|---|---|
| Sample Name | A-E |
| Lab Number | 6836 |
| Water Used | DI |
| pH | 7.6 |
| Phosphorus | < 0.1 |
| Calcium | 17.4 |
| Magnesium | 3.9 |
| Potassium | 4.6 |
| Sodium | 2.1 |
| Sulfur | 1.7 |
| Boron | 0.05 |
| Iron | 1.5 |
| Manganese | < 0.02 |
| Copper | < 0.02 |
| Zinc | < 0.02 |
| Aluminum | 3.8 |
| Molybdenum | 0.19 |
| Cobalt | 0.01 |
| Calcium % | 62.1% |
| Magnesium % | 13.9% |
| Potassium % | 16.3% |
| Sodium % | 7.7% |
| Calcium %:Magnesium % | 4.5 |
| Calcium mEq/L | 0.87 |
| Magnesium mEq/L | 1.45 |
| Potassium mEq/L | 0.46 |
| Sodium mEq/L | 0.79 |

**Fig. 77** *The nutrient availability is quite low on the paste test with phosphorus, along with manganese, copper and zinc, below the detection limit (<0.02) in spite of the extremely high levels shown on the standard report.*

## High Exchange Capacity Soils Standard and Paste Test Example 12: Ohio Agriculture Field D-1 & 2 Samples Good (A) & Poor

This is a field located near Upper Sandusky, Ohio. It is a general agricultural field used for growing corn, beans and wheat. For every crop there are consistent spots in the field that produce poorly and are compact and very tight. This problem shows up especially bad for the corn and beans, which often see a drop in production of 15-30 bushels per acre for the corn and 5-10 bushels per acre for the beans. There are no glaring differences when comparing the data on the standard test (Figure 78). In fact the poor sample is better in virtually every aspect of the soil test. This is not uncommon since the removal rates are lower from the lack of production. The poor areas represent less than 10% of the whole field but can be easily picked out while the crop is growing and from the yield map data.

The soluble calcium levels from the paste test (Figure 79) prove to be the major problem in the poor areas. This is much the same issue that I had on the Bernath potato farm (Figure 20 & 21), however that proved to be a spreading problem and this is more a soil type issue.

The pH is low, and I would start by spreading between 1,500 and 2,000 pounds per acre of dolomite lime. The lime alone might temporarily cover up the problem for a year, but it wouldn't be long before the poor spots start showing up again. Along with the lime I would apply 1,200-1,500 pounds of gypsum only on the poor areas. Incorporating the lime and gypsum with some aggressive tillage would speed up the improvement of the poor areas. If this farm were being tested too late in the fall to do the tillage and get a cover crop growing, then tilling just the poor areas with the lime and gypsum in the spring would be a big help.

Phosphorus applied at around 100 pounds of $P_2O_5$ over removal rates with possibly 40-50 pounds of $P_2O_5$ in a row starter would be ideal especially since lime may be left on the surface. If a starter could not be used, I would not broadcast the lime until fall. Apply the gypsum on the poor areas and broadcast the $P_2O_5$ fertilizer over the entire field. Work the poor areas after everything has been applied to get good incorporation.

Two hundred pounds of muriate of potash (0-0-60) would cover removal rates for most general crops and also leave a small amount for buildup too.

Broadcasting 10 pounds of zinc sulfate along with foliar feeding zinc and possibly adding copper would be my initial course of action for the trace elements. Naturally a tissue analysis would be the best for deciding the direction of a foliar program. Applying some molybdenum on soybeans should be considered since the solubility is below the detection limit (<0.01).

# High Exchange Capacity Soils Standard Test
## Example 12: Ohio Agriculture Field D-1 & 2
## Samples Good (A) & Poor

| Sample Location | | D-1&2 | D-1&2 |
|---|---|---|---|
| Sample ID | | A | Poor |
| Lab Number | | 139 | 140 |
| Sample Depth (inches) | | 9 | 9 |
| Total Exchange Capacity (m.e.) | | 12.62 | 12.72 |
| pH of Soil Sample | | 5.60 | 5.60 |
| Organic Matter (percent) | | 3.04 | 2.88 |
| Anions | SULFUR: p.p.m. | 16 | 18 |
| | Mehlich III Phosphorus: as ($P_2O_5$) lbs. / acre | 105 | 163 |
| Exchangeable Cations | CALCIUM: lbs. / acre  Value Found | 3996 | 3777 |
| | MAGNESIUM: lbs. / acre  Value Found | 484 | 630 |
| | POTASSIUM: lbs. / acre  Value Found | 414 | 463 |
| | SODIUM: lbs. / acre | 50 | 41 |
| Base Saturation % | Calcium (60 to 70%) | 52.76 | 49.48 |
| | Magnesium (10 to 20%) | 10.65 | 13.76 |
| | Potassium (2 to 5%) | 2.80 | 3.11 |
| | Sodium (0.5 to 3%) | 0.57 | 0.46 |
| | Other Bases (Variable) | 6.20 | 6.20 |
| | Exchangeable Hydrogen (10 to 15%) | 27.00 | 27.00 |
| Trace Elements | Boron (ppm) | 0.38 | 0.39 |
| | Iron (ppm) | 140 | 147 |
| | Manganese (ppm) | 65 | 108 |
| | Copper (ppm) | 1.47 | 1.4 |
| | Zinc (ppm) | 2.52 | 2.29 |
| | Aluminum (ppm) | 697 | 669 |

**Fig. 78** *There are no glaring differences when comparing the data on the standard test for the two samples. In fact the poor sample is better in virtually every aspect of the soil test.*

# High Exchange Capacity Soils Paste Test
# Example 12: Ohio Agriculture Field D-1 & 2
# Samples Good (A) & Poor

| Sample Location | D-1&2 | D-1&2 |
|---|---|---|
| Sample Name | A | Poor |
| Lab Number | 7510 | 7511 |
| Water Used | DI | DI |
| pH | 5.6 | 5.6 |
| Phosphorus | < 0.1 | < 0.1 |
| Calcium | 26.9 | 8 |
| Magnesium | 2.3 | 3.6 |
| Potassium | 4.6 | 7.9 |
| Sodium | 2.2 | 2.7 |
| Sulfur | 2.6 | 3.1 |
| Boron | 0.31 | 0.32 |
| Iron | 5.73 | 10.17 |
| Manganese | 0.07 | 0.19 |
| Copper | 0.03 | 0.02 |
| Zinc | < 0.02 | 0.03 |
| Aluminum | 1.6 | 1.6 |
| Molybdenum | < 0.01 | < 0.01 |
| Cobalt | < 0.01 | < 0.01 |
| Calcium % | 74.7% | 36.0% |
| Magnesium % | 6.3% | 16.5% |
| Potassium % | 12.8% | 35.6% |
| Sodium % | 6.2% | 12.0% |
| Calcium %:Magnesium % | 11.9 | 2.2 |
| Calcium mEq/L | 1.34 | 0.40 |
| Magnesium mEq/L | 2.24 | 0.66 |
| Potassium mEq/L | 0.71 | 0.21 |
| Sodium mEq/L | 1.22 | 0.36 |

**Fig. 79** *The paste test shows that the soluble calcium levels prove to be the major problem in the poor areas.*

# Chapter 7

# Irrigation Water and Its Impact on Soil Balance

THE QUALITY OF IRRIGATION WATER IS AN EXTREMELY IMPORTANT consideration when balancing soils. Rainwater is relatively inert with virtually no cations or anions. Rain falling through the atmosphere could dissolve sulfur dioxide or carbon dioxide gases and through chemical reactions convert these products into a weak sulfuric or carbonic acid. This does happen frequently, particularly around heavily industrialize areas, which results in lowering the pH of the water.

Unlike the past, stricter air quality standards have greatly reduced this issue to the point that many now have to buy sulfur as a soil additive. This is certainly not a bad thing. But don't overlook the fact that even rainwater will have an impact on our soil balance. For purposes of discussion here, I will consider rainwater to be similar to the distilled water created in the laboratory.

A paste analysis using distilled water from the laboratory will reflect fairly accurately what is happening in the soil solution. But after irrigation starts all bets about what is happening in the soil solution are off. Once turned on, the irrigation water will start to take control of the soil solution immediately. The lower the exchange capacity of the soil—and consequently the lower the buffering capacity—the faster this happens. Even soils with a good buffering capacity will begin to change after only a few irrigation cycles.

# Water Analysis Interpretation

Interpretation of a water report can seem rather overwhelming at first glance. There is a lot of good information on a report but I would like to take just the cation portion and give you an idea how I like to approach the numbers.

Below are two actual water analyses used on two different golf courses in the United States. The first thing that I like to do when looking at a water report is calculate the saturation levels of nutrients in the water. This is done by adding up all the cations (mEq/L) and finding a total. In these examples, well #1 has a total of 23.58 versus the lake sample with only 1.98 mEq/L. Dividing each of the cations (mEq/L) by the total (mEq/L) and multiplying by 100, the percent saturation for each cation can be calculated.

## Water Analysis

### Well #1

| Cation | ppm | mEq/L | % Saturation |
|---|---|---|---|
| Calcium | 106.2 | 5.31 | 22.5 |
| Magnesium | 57.8 | 4.81 | 20.4 |
| Potassium | 20.2 | 0.52 | 2.2 |
| Sodium | 297.7 | 12.94 | 52.9 |
| Total | | 23.58 | |

### Lake

| Cation | ppm | mEq/L | % Saturation |
|---|---|---|---|
| Calcium | 26.2 | 1.31 | 66.2 |
| Magnesium | 2.4 | 0.2 | 0.1 |
| Potassium | 6.3 | 0.16 | 0.1 |
| Sodium | 39.6 | 1.72 | 33.6 |
| Total | | 1.98 | |

This is basically the same way the laboratory calculates the base saturation on the standard test and the percent of cations on the paste test.

By looking at the percent saturation numbers we now know which direction the irrigation is going to drive our soil balance. In both of these cases the balance is not good. The speed at which the soil balance will move to that of the water will depend upon the buffering capacity of the soil. A higher exchange capacity, which is a function of clay and organic matter, results in a higher buffering capacity and the ability to resist change. Therefore, sandy soils will move toward the balance of the water very quickly. Even well buffered soils will move toward the balance of the water after a series of applications. Although the balance of nutrients is not very good in well #1, the water in and of itself will supply adequate calcium, magnesium and potassium for plant growth. However if the soils are not continually flushed, a buildup of salts will cause a raft of other problems.

The lake water is very clean by comparison to the wellwater, but its balance will eventually lead to magnesium and potassium deficiencies. Improper watering regimes can ultimately lead to a buildup of salts and/or poor soil balance. Analyzing your various water sources can help head off nutritional problems through advanced fertilizer applications or fertigation. Remember, running a paste test with your irrigation water is a great thing to do, but that is like one irrigation cycle. Periodic paste testing through the summer is still the smart way to avoid problems.

*The Soil Probe Newsletter, Logan Labs*

## Low Exchange Capacity Soils Standard Test, Paste Test and Irrigation Water Analysis
## Example 1: Green 16

The following example includes a standard soil test, a paste test, and a water analysis (Figures 80-82). The soil has a very light exchange capacity with a TEC of only 3.22. The paste test, which is using the irrigation water, represents one irrigation cycle. Unfortunately there was not a paste test done with distilled water for comparison. However it is quite apparent after one irrigation cycle how close the saturation of the cations matches the irrigation water. I have calculated what the cation balance might look like after five irrigation cycles if the water was not leached through and removal was not included. The paste cation balance is essentially the same as the water cation balance. The potassium balance is what really takes the hit in this situation. Adding potassium before and during irrigation would be helpful for maintaining adequate levels in the plants.

Oftentimes disease pressure increases once irrigation starts. The reduction in potassium availability could be directly related to this problem. As calcium increases along with the bicarbonates, soluble phosphorus tends to precipitate out. The result is a reduction of energy in the plants, which drastically reduces growth rates. This irrigation water example has only 232 ppm salt concentration (Figure 81). This level does not appear to be a problem on the surface, but after four to five irrigation cycles without any flushing, the buildup will quickly approach 1,000 ppm. As the salt concentration increases, more energy is needed to bring water and nutrients in against the concentration gradient—consequently the need for phosphorus increases. Irrigating with water that has marginal quality in combination with short irrigation cycles is burning the candle at both ends and a sure setup for future trouble.

# Low Exchange Capacity Soils Standard Test
## Example 1: Green 16

| | | | Green |
|---|---|---|---|
| Sample Location | | | Green |
| Sample ID | | | 16 |
| Lab Number | | | 39 |
| Sample Depth (inches) | | | 6 |
| Total Exchange Capacity (m.e.) | | | 3.22 |
| pH of Soil Sample | | | 7.10 |
| Organic Matter (percent) | | | 1.27 |
| **Anions** | **SULFUR:** | p.p.m. | 24 |
| | **Mohlich III Phosphorus:** | as ($P_2O_5$) lbs. / acre | 277 |
| **Exchangeable Cations** | **CALCIUM:** lbs. / acre | Desired Value | 877 |
| | | Value Found | 970 |
| | | Deficit | |
| | **MAGNESIUM:** lbs. / acre | Desired Value | 200 |
| | | Value Found | 111 |
| | | Deficit | -89 |
| | **POTASSIUM:** lbs. / acre | Desired Value | 200 |
| | | Value Found | 109 |
| | | Deficit | -91 |
| | **SODIUM:** | lbs. / acre | 27 |
| **Base Saturation %** | Calcium (60 to 70%) | | 75.19 |
| | Magnesium (10 to 20%) | | 14.34 |
| | Potassium (2 to 5%) | | 4.33 |
| | Sodium (0.5 to 3%) | | 1.82 |
| | Other Bases (Variable) | | 4.30 |
| | Exchangeable Hydrogen (10 to 15%) | | 0.00 |
| **Trace Elements** | Boron (ppm) | | 0.23 |
| | Iron (ppm) | | 77 |
| | Manganese (ppm) | | 42 |
| | Copper (ppm) | | 1.46 |
| | Zinc (ppm) | | 13.75 |
| | Aluminum (ppm) | | 189 |

**Fig. 80** *The soil has a very light exchange capacity with a TEC of only 3.22. The lower the exchange capacity of the soil, the lower the buffering capacity.*

# Low Exchange Capacity Soils
## Irrigation Water Analysis

**Sample Location:** Irrigation

| | | | | | |
|---|---|---|---|---|---|
| *pH* | | 7.8 | | | |
| *Hardness* | *ppm* | 124.2 | | | |
| *Hardness Grains* | */gal* | 7.26 | | | |
| *Conductivity* | *mmhos/cm* | 0.36 | | | |
| *Sodium Adsorption Ratio* | | 1.12 | | | |

| | | *p.p.m.* | *mEq/L* | *lbs./A IN* | *Base Saturation* |
|---|---|---|---|---|---|
| *Calcium* | *Ca* | 31 | 1.55 | 7.05 | 37% |
| *Magnesium* | *Mg* | 11.4 | 0.95 | 2.58 | 23% |
| *Potassium* | *K* | 3.1 | 0.08 | 0.71 | 2% |
| *Sodium* | *Na* | 36.7 | 1.60 | 8.34 | 38% |
| *Iron* | *Fe* | 0.2 | | 0.04 | |
| | | | 4.18 | | |

| | | | *mEq/L* | *lbs./A IN* | |
|---|---|---|---|---|---|
| *Total Alkalinity* | | 129.0 | | 29.32 | |
| *Carbonate* | | 0.0 | 0.00 | 0.00 | |
| *Bicarbonate* | | 157.0 | 2.57 | 35.68 | |
| *Chloride* | | 53.0 | 1.50 | 12.05 | |
| *Sulfate* | | 20.3 | 0.43 | 4.62 | |
| *Salt Concentration* | | 232.3 | | 52.80 | |
| *Boron* | | 0.02 | | | |
| *Cation/Anion Ratio* | | | 0.93 | | |
| *Nitrate* | | 2.5 | | | |

**Fig. 81** *This irrigation water example has only 232 ppm salt concentration. This level does not appear to be a problem on the surface, but after four to five irrigation cycles without any flushing, the buildup will quickly approach 1,000 ppm. As the salt concentration increases, more energy is needed to bring water and nutrients in against the concentration gradient.*

# Low Exchange Capacity Soils Paste Test
## Example 1: Green 16

| Sample Location | | | Green 16 |
|---|---|---|---|
| | | | |
| Lab Number | | | 22786 |
| Water Used | | | Irrigation |
| pH | | | 7 |
| Soluble Salts | | ppm | 327 |
| Chloride (Cl) | | ppm | 68 |
| Bicarbonate (HCO$_3$) | | ppm | 229 |
| Anions | SULFUR | ppm | 31.68 |
| | PHOSPHORUS | ppm | 1.44 |
| Soluble Cations | CALCIUM | ppm | 36.75 |
| | | meq/l | 1.84 |
| | MAGNESIUM | ppm | 9.5 |
| | | meq/l | 0.79 |
| | POTASSIUM | ppm | 33.23 |
| | | meq/l | 0.86 |
| | SODIUM | ppm | 45.47 |
| | | meq/l | 1.98 |
| Percent | Calcium | | 33.60 |
| | Magnesium | | 14.47 |
| | Potassium | | 15.78 |
| | Sodium | | 36.15 |
| Trace Elements | Boron (ppm) | | 0.14 |
| | Iron (ppm) | | 0.44 |
| | Manganese (ppm) | | 0.53 |
| | Copper (ppm) | | 0.03 |
| | Zinc (ppm) | | 0.08 |
| | Aluminum (ppm) | | 0.96 |

**Fig. 82** *The paste test, which is using the irrigation water, represents one irrigation cycle. It is quite apparent, even after one cycle, how close the saturation of the cations matches the level in the irrigation water.*

Low Exchange Capacity Soils Standard Test,
Two Paste Tests (Distilled and Irrigation)
and Irrigation Water Analysis
Example 2: RBA

This example shows the results of a standard soil test, irrigation water and two paste test analyses. One paste test uses distilled water and other using the on-site irrigation water. The combination of these four tests will provide the best soil results information needed to grow everything from turfgrass to tomatoes. In this example, the standard soil test indicates a very light exchange capacity soil with almost no organic matter. Consequently, there will be virtually no buffering capacity and once irrigation starts; the quality of the irrigation water will control the balance of the soil solution.

The standard test on the soil shows deficits in calcium, magnesium and potassium. The desired calcium level, which is set by the laboratory, is even below my preference of 1,200 lbs. per acre. Phosphorus is below my strategic level of 250 lbs. per acre. Trace elements are all low but manganese is especially low (Figure 83). There is no question that we are going to supplement some nutrients and preferably in more than one application. With the results of only the standard soil test to consider, I would be thinking of 1,000 lbs. of dolomite lime per acre, some phosphorus and potassium at 100 lbs. per acre over the removal rate and a trace element program of broadcasted boron, manganese, copper and zinc along with some foliar applications.

The paste test done with distilled water (Figure 85) indicates the nutrient solution for the plants prior to irrigation. The pH remains 6.1, but could be lower depending on the pH of the rainwater. The phosphorus is quite good in solution, and based on this paste test data I would scale back my phosphorus application to just applying the crop removal rates. The calcium and magnesium are very low and the application of a fine dolomite lime would fit in nicely. The potassium is low but better than one might expect based on the standard test. I would stick with the potassium application of removal rates plus add 100 lbs. per acre of either 0-0-60 or 0-0-50. The extra potassium is added for two reasons. First, the application of dolomite lime will put competing cations of calcium and magnesium in solution. Secondly, the feed rate may not be very good based on what is found in the standard test. The trace element program based on the standard test would remain in place with the exclusion of boron. Iron along with the rest of the traces would be included in a foliar program.

The paste test using irrigation water (Figure 86) abruptly starts to change the balance toward that of the irrigation water, which is not very good. Overall the water is fairly clean as far as the amounts of cations being added, but the balance of the solution is heavily weighted toward sodium. Short watering cycles will quickly build the cations up in favor of sodium so trying to offset that issue with some gypsum and K-Mag applications would be good. The best thing would be to flush the profile with irrigation water every four to five cycles. Using a good soil surfactant prior to flushing the soil would enhance the movement of water through the profile. Assuming these samples were collected in the fall or early spring, I would still apply the dolomite lime as a cheap source of calcium and magnesium, even though the solubility of the lime would drop to 5-10% once the high pH water was applied. The pH of the paste sample using irrigation water is just two-tenths below that of the water. This drop indicates the low buffering capacity of the soil. After a couple of watering cycles the pH will seek that of the water. I have mentioned earlier that irrigation water can act somewhat like an extracting solution. This is demonstrated by the slight increase in the calcium, magnesium and potassium levels on the paste test using irrigation water when compared to those values you get when adding the values from the distilled water paste to the values in the irrigation water. This doesn't happen to sodium since it is so soluble. You can practically add the level of sodium in the irrigation water to a distilled water paste extract and come up with the level in the irrigation water paste extract. This extracting effect of irrigation water will tend to strip the most soluble nutrients from the soil over time, especially in a climate where there are good leaching rains during the year.

The phosphorus solubility is virtually cut in half with one irrigation cycle when using high pH water. This can be seen when comparing the distilled paste extract to the irrigation water paste extract. This reduction of soluble phosphorus will continue as the irrigation water is used. Therefore, adding soluble phosphorus to the fertility program will help offset this problem. The use of products like humic acids will enhance the availability of phosphorus to the plants. Foliar feeding phosphorus would be effective, except for golf course greens and tees that are being cut extremely short on a daily basis.

The high pH irrigation water drastically reduced the solubility of boron. When the irrigation water was being used, boron and the rest of the traces should be foliar fed on a two to three week schedule. Even though iron increased on the paste test using irrigation water, I would keep it in the foliar program since bicarbonates could increase, reducing the availability of iron.

In conclusion, the irrigation water will have a dramatic effect on nutrient solubility. Fertility programs should be adjusted to compensate for the reduction or increase in nutrient availability. This level of testing would not have to be done every year, but a program of monitoring should be put in place to keep heading in the right direction and avoid problems.

# Low Exchange Capacity Soils Standard Test
# Example 2: RBA

| Sample Location | | | RBA |
|---|---|---|---|
| | | | |
| Lab Number | | | 26 |
| Sample Depth (inches) | | | 6 |
| Total Exchange Capacity (m.e.) | | | 3.75 |
| pH of Soil Sample | | | 6.10 |
| Organic Matter (percent) | | | 0.56 |
| Anions | SULFUR: | p.p.m. | 13 |
| | Mehlich III Phosphorus: | as ($P_2O_5$) lbs. / acre | 210 |
| Exchangeable Cations | CALCIUM: lbs. / acre | Desired Value | 1020 |
| | | Value Found | 913 |
| | | Deficit | -107 |
| | MAGNESIUM: lbs. / acre | Desired Value | 200 |
| | | Value Found | 124 |
| | | Deficit | -76 |
| | POTASSIUM: lbs. / acre | Desired Value | 200 |
| | | Value Found | 76 |
| | | Deficit | -124 |
| | SODIUM: | lbs. / acre | 73 |
| Base Saturation % | Calcium (60 to 70%) | | 60.81 |
| | Magnesium (10 to 20%) | | 13.76 |
| | Potassium (2 to 5%) | | 2.60 |
| | Sodium (0.5 to 3%) | | 4.20 |
| | Other Bases (Variable) | | 5.20 |
| | Exchangeable Hydrogen (10 to 15%) | | 13.50 |
| Trace Elements | Boron (ppm) | | 0.41 |
| | Iron (ppm) | | 95 |
| | Manganese (ppm) | | 7 |
| | Copper (ppm) | | 1.29 |
| | Zinc (ppm) | | 4.62 |
| | Aluminum (ppm) | | 140 |

**Fig. 83** *The standard soil test indicates a very light exchange capacity soil with almost no organic matter. Consequently, there will be virtually no buffering capacity. Once the irrigation starts the quality of the irrigation water will control the balance of the soil solution. The standard test on the soil shows deficits in calcium, magnesium and potassium.*

# Low Exchange Capacity Soils
## Irrigation Water Analysis

| Sample Location: RBA | | | | |
|---|---|---|---|---|
| pH | | 7.6 | | |
| Hardness | ppm | 61.8 | | |
| Hardness Grains | /gal | 3.61 | | |
| Conductivity | mmhos/cm | 0.31 | | |
| Sodium Adsorption Ratio | | 1.28 | | |
| | | **p.p.m.** | **mEq/L** | **lbs./A IN** |
| Calcium | Ca | 16 | 0.80 | 3.64 |
| Magnesium | Mg | 5.3 | 0.44 | 1.20 |
| Potassium | K | 1.2 | 0.03 | 0.27 |
| Sodium | Na | 29.6 | 1.29 | 6.74 |
| Iron | Fe | 0.3 | | 0.08 |
| | | | 2.56 | |
| | | | **mEq/L** | **lbs./A IN** |
| Total Alkalinity | | 43.0 | | 9.77 |
| Carbonate | | 0.0 | 0.00 | 0.00 |
| Bicarbonate | | 52.0 | 0.85 | 11.82 |
| Chloride | | 20.0 | 0.57 | 4.55 |
| Sulfate | | 20.6 | 0.43 | 4.68 |
| Salt Concentration | | 198.4 | | 45.09 |
| Boron | | < 0.02 | | |
| Cation/Anion Ratio | | | 1.38 | |

Cation Water Balance

    31% Calcium
    17% Magnesium
    1% Potassium
    51% Sodium

**Fig. 84** *The irrigation water analysis shows that the high pH of the irrigation water drastically reduced the solubility of boron. Consequently the recommendation is that when irrigation water is being used, boron and the rest of the traces should be foliar fed on a 2-3 week schedule.*

# Low Exchange Capacity Soils Paste Test
## Example 2: RBA Distilled

| Sample Location | | | RBA |
|---|---|---|---|
| | | | |
| Lab Number | | | 25994 |
| Water Used | | | DI |
| pH | | | 6.1 |
| Soluble Salts | | ppm | 79 |
| Chloride (Cl) | | ppm | 38 |
| Bicarbonate ($HCO_3$) | | ppm | 56 |
| Anions | SULFUR | ppm | 5.11 |
| | PHOSPHORUS | ppm | 1.62 |
| Soluble Cations | CALCIUM | ppm | 7.42 |
| | | meq/l | 0.37 |
| | MAGNESIUM | ppm | 1.28 |
| | | meq/l | 0.11 |
| | POTASSIUM | ppm | 9.99 |
| | | meq/l | 0.26 |
| | SODIUM | ppm | 9.11 |
| | | meq/l | 0.40 |
| Percent | Calcium | | 32.74 |
| | Magnesium | | 9.42 |
| | Potassium | | 22.89 |
| | Sodium | | 34.95 |
| Trace Elements | Boron (ppm) | | 0.27 |
| | Iron (ppm) | | 0.5 |
| | Manganese (ppm) | | < 0.02 |
| | Copper (ppm) | | < 0.02 |
| | Zinc (ppm) | | < 0.02 |
| | Aluminum (ppm) | | 1.36 |

**Fig. 85** *The phosphorus is quite good in solution and based on this paste data. The calcium and magnesium are very low and an application of a fine dolomite lime would fit in nicely. The potassium is low, but better than one might expect based on the results found on the standard test.*

# Low Exchange Capacity Soils Paste Test
## Example 2: RBA Irrigation

| Sample Location | | | RBA |
|---|---|---|---|
| | | | |
| Lab Number | | | 25865 |
| Water Used | | | RBA |
| pH | | | 7.4 |
| Soluble Salts | | ppm | 219 |
| Chloride (Cl) | | ppm | 35 |
| Bicarbonate (HCO$_3$) | | ppm | 41 |
| Anions | SULFUR | ppm | 18.41 |
| | PHOSPHORUS | ppm | 0.85 |
| Soluble Cations | CALCIUM | ppm | 17.98 |
| | | meq/l | 0.90 |
| | MAGNESIUM | ppm | 4.49 |
| | | meq/l | 0.37 |
| | POTASSIUM | ppm | 14.89 |
| | | meq/l | 0.39 |
| | SODIUM | ppm | 37.66 |
| | | meq/l | 1.64 |
| Percent | Calcium | | 27.27 |
| | Magnesium | | 11.34 |
| | Potassium | | 11.73 |
| | Sodium | | 49.66 |
| Trace Elements | Boron (ppm) | | 0.03 |
| | Iron (ppm) | | 1.01 |
| | Manganese (ppm) | | 0.05 |
| | Copper (ppm) | | < 0.02 |
| | Zinc (ppm) | | < 0.02 |
| | Aluminum (ppm) | | 4.29 |

**Fig. 86** *Overall the water is fairly clean as far as the amounts of cations being added are concerned, but the balance of the solution is heavily weighted toward sodium. The pH of the paste sample using irrigation water is just two-tenths below that of the water analysis. This minute difference indicates the low buffering capacity of the soil.*

# Chapter 8

# Interpreting Tissue Analysis

PLANT TISSUE ANALYSIS HAS BEEN AROUND FOR A VERY LONG TIME, but it is still not being used nearly enough by consultants, agronomic advisors or growers. Waiting to collect a tissue analysis only when things don't look quite right is a misuse or underuse of the available technology. Often there is a problem in trying to understand the data when it gets back from the laboratory. All too often the good and bad samples look almost alike and comparisons are not possible. Plants tend to grow to the potential of the least available nutrient (lowest common denominator). Therefore tissue analysis really only is best utilized in conjunction with soil and paste analysis. This chapter will give you insight into how an agronomist would interpret the results of tissue analysis.

Tissue analysis is the only way to technically evaluate how well  your soil fertility program is doing. Not doing tissue analysis is like a professor teaching students and never giving an exam. Exams are useful for two different reasons. First they give students an opportunity to find out what they have learned, and second is to show the professor how well he or she has presented the material. The benefit is that based on the test results, solid, sensible and evidence-based adjustments can then be made. Just like students, crops differ greatly and may require  a different approach depending on any number of different situations.

Genetically crops are being altered at an extremely rapid rate. It is naive and irresponsible to think that what we did twenty or even ten years ago is still an acceptable practice today. How we handle soil fertility issues is best managed by depending upon information that is gleaned from tissue analysis. Fertilizing soils based entirely upon a visual plant analysis alone is just as bad as relying only on soil analysis.

Tissue analysis is a great way to verify soil additive claims. I am sure everyone has heard many claims about using this or that product will release nutrients locked up in the soil. What better way to find out than to use a tissue analysis and plant weights to really see if this is true.

This guide to understanding tissue analysis (from an agronomist's point of view) is probably a very different approach than that from which a plant physiologist might take.

The place to always start is with the established tissue guidelines. Keep in mind though that many of these guidelines were set up over 40 years ago. Therefore we may need to constantly tweak the numbers to achieve maximum quality and production. I believe that one of the most important steps in tissue analysis is being able to relate the data back to plant weight. Plants adjust their growth based on the least available nutrient and therefore will slow down growth and size to match their nutrient feed uptake. It is for this reason that when good and bad tissue samples are analyzed, they come back from the lab looking very close to the same.

When it comes to plants, bigger is generally better, with healthier and larger plants tending to provide bigger yields. Therefore when sampling tissues, it is imperative to collect the same number of leaves or plants and weigh them. Even though you may not be comparing tissue within a field, you will be comparing them to your healthy, high-yielding crop standard. Figure 87 shows a weight range of corn plants collected at the pre-6 leaf collar stage for whole plants and at the 7- leaf collar stage.

## Corn Plant Weights at Various Maturity Stages

|  | 3-Leaf Collar | 4-Leaf Collar | 5-Leaf Collar | 6-Leaf Collar | 7-Leaf Collar Leaves |
| --- | --- | --- | --- | --- | --- |
| Range | 53-83 | 54-162 | 127-387 | 358-927 | 104-117 |
| Total | 141.8 | 2691.5 | 8966.2 | 9703.4 | 332.3 |
| Number | 2 | 26 | 38 | 15 | 3 |
| Average | 70.9 | 103.5 | 236.0 | 646.9 | 110.8 |

**Fig. 87** *Corn plant weights (grams per 12 samples) at various maturity stages.*

You can see there is wide range of weights within the various maturities of the corn plants collected at the pre-6 leaf collar stages. This range varies as much as 300 percent. This data was collected over one season and tissue analysis was preformed on each composite sample of 12 plants or leaves. The weight range narrows considerably when sampling only the leaves and this sampling probably would not be necessary unless you are making a comparison between good and bad plants.

The range of the nutrients varies about 200% for the whole plants, but narrows somewhat when just looking at the leaves. When examining the data for individual samples the heaviest plants usually do not have the highest nutrient values. The lighter samples have some of the highest nutrient numbers. Therefore comparing all these samples on an equal basis without adjusting for the weight for the whole plant samples is like comparing a 300-pound mini-horse to a 2,000-pound drafthorse. The horse blood analysis would be very comparable, but the level of work that could be done by each horse would be vastly different.

This adjustment by weight is really only practical for crops planted on an individual basis like corn. Wheat could be done, but it would be very time consuming. For turfgrass, tissue numbers could be adjusted by clipping weight. It would not be very practical to collect whole fields, but collecting sample areas and calculating that to the whole field, green or tee could be done without too much problem.

Why sample this early in the crop maturity anyway? Grass crops such as corn and wheat determine some of their yield very early. Corn, for instance, is determining the number of ear kernel rows around the 6-leaf collar stage. It would also be good to sample corn at the tassling stage—another critical time in which ear length is being determined.

## Corn Nutrient Range for Nitrogen, Phosphorus and Potassium at Various Maturity Stages

| Growth Stage | Nutrient Range | | |
| --- | --- | --- | --- |
| | % Nitrogen | % Phosphorus | % Potassium |
| 4-Leaf Collar | 3.38-5.11 | 0.24-0.46 | 2.51-5.16 |
| 5-Leaf Collar | 2.82-5.42 | 0.26-0.52 | 2.07-5.20 |
| 6-Leaf Collar | 2.98-4.69 | 0.24-0.39 | 1.53-4.43 |
| 7-Leaf Collar Leaves | 3.13-4.23 | 0.26-0.32 | 1.68-3.56 |

**Fig. 88** *The corn nutrient range for NPK at various maturities.*

Soybean yields are determined during the back third of the season so I tend to hold off tissue sampling until that time unless something is restricting the growth during the earlier vegetative stage. Tissue sampling is best done prior to the critical times in the crop lifecycle.

Figures 89, 90 and 91 show the desired nutrient levels for corn, beans and wheat at different critical maturity stages. The corn data in Figure 89 also has some suggested weights for a 12 plant sampling. If, for example, your sample of corn at the 5-leaf collar stage weighs 165 grams, which is 50% of the ideal, then cut all your tissue data in half and see which nutrients are the lowest compared to the nutrient standards given. Remember nutrients like zinc can help the uptake of phosphorus in the grasses and manganese can help soybeans pick up many nutrients. The point is nutrient relationships are very complex and we must not assume that a phosphorus deficiency in the plant needs to be fixed with an application of phosphorus—especially if the soil levels appear to be adequate.

With a standard soil test the amount of exchangeable nutrients in the soil is known. A paste test tells what is in solution and now we know that the tissue test tells us how well the nutrients are being picked up out of the solution. Using a combination of testing tools such as the standard and paste soil test along with tissue analysis will go a long way toward understanding crop production issues.

Ultimately all crop production issues can come back to nutritional problems. Unfortunately these crop production problems, whether quality or quantity issues, are not always related to the level of nutrients in a soil. Diseases or root pruning caused by insects can easily restrict nutrient uptake too. Also remember that compaction is still the top reason for limiting nutrient uptake.

Figure 88 shows a seed treatment test that I was working on in 2007. Although there were large differences in weights and nutrient levels at 6-leaf collar stage, the yields were essentially the same at harvest with the exception of the outside 6 rows. The outside 6 rows received limited compaction. I have in the past tested the soil in the outside 15 feet and found it to have poorer fertility than the center of the field. The compaction, along with fertility shortages in the center of the field, neutralized the gains set up by the seed treatment.

Many of the disease issues in crops are nutritionally related. I am certainly not qualified to discuss this topic in much depth, but the book *Mineral Nutrition and Plant Disease* written by a number of authors and edited by Datnoff, Elmer and Huber is certainly a book that should be in everyone's personal library. Personally I have seen that fungicide applications on soybeans have not yielded much response, especially where a foliar application of manganese was applied to improve plant nutrition.

# The Desired Nutrient Levels for Corn
## at the Six Growth Stages

**3-Leaf Collar Stage 80 gm/12 plants**

| | % Ca | % Mg | % P | % K | % N | % S | ppm B | ppm Cu | ppm Fe | ppm Mn | ppm Zn |
|---|---|---|---|---|---|---|---|---|---|---|---|
| Desired Levels | 0.65 | 0.31 | 0.43 | 3.40 | 4.25 | 0.3 | 11.0 | 11.0 | 75.0 | 70.0 | 50.0 |

**4-Leaf Collar Stage 140 gm/12 plants**

| | % Ca | % Mg | % P | % K | % N | % S | ppm B | ppm Cu | ppm Fe | ppm Mn | ppm Zn |
|---|---|---|---|---|---|---|---|---|---|---|---|
| Desired Levels | 0.6 | 0.29 | 0.41 | 3.23 | 4.07 | 0.29 | 10.4 | 10.5 | 71.4 | 66.3 | 47.6 |

**5-Leaf Collar Stage 330 gm/12 plants**

| | % Ca | % Mg | % P | % K | % N | % S | ppm B | ppm Cu | ppm Fe | ppm Mn | ppm Zn |
|---|---|---|---|---|---|---|---|---|---|---|---|
| Desired Levels | 0.55 | 0.27 | 0.39 | 3.06 | 3.89 | 0.28 | 9.7 | 10.1 | 68.0 | 62.6 | 45.1 |

**6-Leaf Collar Stage 825 gm/12 plants**

| | % Ca | % Mg | % P | % K | % N | % S | ppm B | ppm Cu | ppm Fe | ppm Mn | ppm Zn |
|---|---|---|---|---|---|---|---|---|---|---|---|
| Desired Levels | 0.50 | 0.25 | 0.34 | 2.80 | 3.71 | 0.25 | 9.0 | 9.5 | 64.0 | 59.0 | 42.0 |

**7-Leaf Collar Stage**

| | % Ca | % Mg | % P | % K | % N | % S | ppm B | ppm Cu | ppm Fe | ppm Mn | ppm Zn |
|---|---|---|---|---|---|---|---|---|---|---|---|
| Desired Levels | 0.45 | 0.22 | 0.28 | 2.60 | 3.54 | 0.24 | 8.5 | 9.1 | 60.0 | 55.1 | 40.3 |

**Ear Leaf**

| | % Ca | % Mg | % P | % K | % N | % S | ppm B | ppm Cu | ppm Fe | ppm Mn | ppm Zn |
|---|---|---|---|---|---|---|---|---|---|---|---|
| Desired Levels | 0.60 | 0.20 | 0.28 | 2.21 | 3.00 | 0.23 | 6.60 | 7.70 | 50.0 | 44.0 | 33.0 |

**Fig. 89** *Desired nutrient levels for corn at various stages of maturity.*

# The Desired Nutrient Levels for Soybeans
## at the Three Growth Stages

| | % Ca | % Mg | % P | % K | % N | % S | B ppm | Cu ppm | Fe ppm | Mn ppm | Zn ppm |
|---|---|---|---|---|---|---|---|---|---|---|---|
| Desired Levels **Pre-Bloom** | 1.3 | 0.5 | 0.45 | 2.70 | 5.2 | 0.26 | 40.0 | 15.0 | 100.0 | 60.0 | 45.0 |
| Desired Levels **Bloom** | 1.10 | 0.40 | 0.40 | 2.50 | 6.00 | 0.30 | 35.0 | 11.0 | 100.0 | 50.0 | 40.0 |
| Desired Levels **Pod Fill** | 0.9 | 0.32 | 0.32 | 2.30 | 5.40 | 0.24 | 28.0 | 8.8 | 80.0 | 40.0 | 32.0 |

**Fig. 90** *Desired nutrient levels for soybeans at various stages of maturity.*

# The Desired Nutrient Levels for Wheat
## at Two Growth Stages

| | N % | P % | K % | S % | Ca % | Mg % | B ppm | Fe ppm | Cu ppm | Mn ppm | Zn ppm |
|---|---|---|---|---|---|---|---|---|---|---|---|
| Desired Level Pre-Joint | 4.2 | 0.46 | 4.4 | 0.30 | 0.47 | 0.16 | 7.0 | 50 | 11.0 | 45.0 | 52.0 |
| Flag Leaf @ Feekes 10 | 3.2 | 0.30 | 3.3 | .25 | 0.50 | 0.12 | 10.0 | 50 | 8.0 | 40.0 | 32.0 |

**Fig. 91** *Desired nutrient levels for wheat at two maturity stages.*

There are many foliar products touted in the industry as the "next best thing to sliced bread." Far too many of these are unproven and sold as some sort of magic bullet. Foliar feeding is very difficult to get consistent results. Fixing one nutrient problem may exacerbate the weakness of another. I have been very suspect of foliar feeding major elements except at critical times or on a continual basis.

Foliar feeding minor elements have worked the best for me, especially those nutrients—such as manganese for beans and zinc for corn—that affect the uptake or upward movement of the major elements. Two criteria must be met when foliar feeding trace elements. First, timing is critical; second, threshold amounts of the metal must be met. Certainly soil levels, evapotranspiration rates, and the root mass that picks up nutrients will determine the threshold amounts of nutrients needed for a foliar program. Maybe this need cannot be economically or physically met by using a foliar application. Personally, I have not been able to make the low-concentration chelates perform as well as the high-concentration flowables. The flowables have their own unique issues when it comes to mixing and spraying, but these are offset by the cost per pound of the metal trace elements and their effectiveness.

Many people want to mix their foliar feed program with their chemical program. The objectives of these two programs though are diametrically opposed to each other. The chemical program wants to maximize the droplet size of the spray so as to minimize drift, but a smaller the droplet size is more desirable for a foliar feed program to get better coverage.

Mixing herbicides and foliar products may not only produce a compatibility issue, but also an efficacy problem for the herbicide, foliar products or both. When in doubt it is always better to spray separately.

# Notes

## Acronyms

Acre furrow slice (AFS)

Anion (negatively charged ion)

Basic cation saturation ratio (BCSR)

Cation exchange capacity (CEC)

Cation (positively charged ion)

Evapotranspiration (ET)

Inductively coupled plasma (ICP)

Milliequivalents (mEq)

Organic matter (OM)

Strategic level of available nutrient (SLAN)

Total exchange capacity (TEC)

Two inches below and two inches off to the side (2 x 2)

## Fertilizer Key

Ammonium nitrate ($NH_4NO_3$) 33-0-0

Ammonium sulfate (($NH_4$)$_2SO_4$) 21-0-0

Anhydrous ammonia ($NH_3$) 82-0-0

Calcium carbonate ($CaCO_3$)

Calcium nitrate ($Ca(NO_3)_2 \cdot 4H_2O$)

Copper sulfate ($CuSO_4 \cdot H_2O$)

Diammonium phosphate (DAP) ($NH_4$)$_2HPO_4$ 18-46-0

Epsom salts, magnesium sulfate ($MgSO_4$)

Gypsum, calcium sulfate ($CaSO_4$)

K-Mag, sul-po-mag (potassium, magnesium and sulfur), 20-22% potassium, 11% magnesium and 20-22% sulfur

Monoammonium phosphate (MAP) $NH_4H_2PO_4$ 11-52-0

Muriate of potash, potassium chloride (KCl) 0-0-60

Potassium sulfate ($K_2SO_4$) 0-0-50

Urea ($CO(NH_2)_2$) 46-0-0

# Index